D1615940

CROSSING THE DELAWARE

The Story of the Delaware Memorial Bridge
The Longest Twin-Suspension Bridge
in the World

by William J. Miller, Jr.

Executive Director,
The Delaware River and Bay Authority

DELAPEAKE
PUBLISHING COMPANY
WILMINGTON, DELAWARE 19899

To my wife Ginny
and our family

Project Coordinator: Ed Golin
Editor: Kathy K. Demarest
Designer: Paul A. Miles
Photographs: Delaware River and Bay Authority

Second Edition, 1984 - Revised

Printed in the United States of America

Library of Congress Card Number: 83-71879

ISBN: 0-911293-02-7 — Hardcover - $9.95
ISBN: 0-911293-01-9 — Paperback - $5.95

Miller, William J.
Crossing the Delaware

Also by William J. Miller

A Ferry Tale —
Crossing the Delaware on the Cape May-Lewes Ferry

William J. Miller has also written extensively about the history, planning, construction and operation of the Cape May-Lewes Ferry. This fascinating account, in hardback and paperback, offers a rich collection of anecdotes and facts about the people, places and events relating to the maritime link between New Jersey and Delaware.

CONTENTS

ANECDOTES

PREFACE

The idea of writing the story of the Delaware Memorial Bridge first occurred to Bill Miller when the construction planning for the second span was underway. The enormity of the project not only greatly impressed him, but everyone who had the chance to discuss the topic, seemed awed.

When service clubs, schools and other groups sought him as the speaker to discuss the bridge construction, their interest was readily apparent.

So, he reasoned, there should be an earnest effort made to record the story. And this he has done for all of us.

On April 12, 1945, as the Lieutenant Governor and President of the Delaware Senate, I worked for and assisted in obtaining the unanimous passage of legislation authorizing the financing for the "Crossing Over the Delaware River."

On August 15, 1951, as the Governor of the State of Delaware, I presided over the opening ceremonies of the Delaware Memorial Bridge. Governor Robert B. Meyner of New Jersey and officials from Delaware, New Jersey, Maryland and other states joined us in celebrating this festive occasion.

February 6, 1963, was another milestone in Delaware River Crossing history when as Governor of Delaware, I joined with Governor Richard J. Hughes of New Jersey at the organizational meeting of the Delaware River and Bay Authority. At that time, the first official provisions were made for the construction of the Twin Span, Delaware Memorial Bridge.

My participation in the planning and bringing to fruition of these impressive transportation links was one of the highlights of my public career.

The interest and enthusiasm demonstrated by William J. Miller, in writing, for all to see, this commentary concerning the history of these important projects is a splendid contribution to the annals of our state.

Bill Miller did all of us a favor in researching and developing this narrative. Not only has he discussed the projects from beginning to end, but the additional information which he has provided concerning incidents at the Bridge gives an insight which will delight those of us who share his interest in these great structures.

Indeed, this document, written by a professional in this field, whom I have known and worked with for more than 35 years, will provide intriguing memories for everyone who admires these monumental engineering feats, which have provided so many benefits to millions of the traveling public.

Elbert N. Carvel
Governor of Delaware, 1949-1953
1961-1965

I join with my old friend and colleague, Delaware's former great Governor Bert Carvel, in commending Executive Director William J. Miller, Jr. for writing this chronicle of the Delaware Memorial Bridge. The busy pressures of modern life make it so easy for us to forget the idealism, vision and dedication of those who had a part in this engineering marvel, which has served so well so many millions of Americans.

Thus, important history of our times is apt to slide into the shadows of things forgotten. This to the loss and disadvantage of those who will be following us over the years, and who would have high interest, and pride, in the recollection of these achievements. And in the identity of those who conceived, and dreamed, and built, and sacrificed and finally achieved.

Bill Miller's chronicle will stem this tide, recording in very readable form the history of the Delaware Memorial Bridge, a source of continuing pride to the citizens of the two States it binds together. As one of those citizens, I thank him for writing it.

Richard J. Hughes
Governor of New Jersey, 1962-1970

Acknowledgments

It would be difficult to adequately express my thanks and appreciation to everyone who assisted in this assignment. Nevertheless, the interest, encouragement and assistance from the commissioners of the Delaware River and Bay Authority, the staff assistance, particularly from the General Manager, Jim Harkins, and his predecessor, Ted Bright, Eleanor Stradley, my secretary, and Rita Migliocco who preceded her, and the typing assistance of Candy Drummond, are most appreciated. I would also like to acknowledge the guidance and advice of Ed Golin, president of Gauge Corporation, the editing and technical assistance of Kathy K. Demarest, editor for Delapeake Publishing Co., and the graphic and layout decisions of Paul A. Miles, designer for Delapeake Publishing Co.

Bill Miller

Cover photograph: *Queen Elizabeth II sails under the Delaware Memorial Bridge (1982) on her first voyage up the Delaware River.*

Chronology of Construction
Delaware Memorial Bridge Twin Span

1945-1947 .... Authorizations from States of Delaware and New Jersey and United States Congress were obtained for construction of Delaware Memorial Bridge.

1948 .... Construction started on first bridge.

August 16, 1951 ...... Opened to traffic at 12:01 a.m.

1958-1963 .... Feasibility and location studies for a second bridge were initiated. State and federal authorization for a second structure obtained.

June 11, 1963 .... Delaware River and Bay Authority voted to proceed with financing and construction of twin span 250 feet north of existing bridge.

April, 1964 .... Construction started on second structure of Delaware Memorial Bridge.

September 12, 1968 ... Opening date of second structure.

1968-1969 .... Modification of first bridge.

December 29, 1969 ... Twin bridges both open to traffic. The original structure now carries traffic into New Jersey and the second structure carries traffic into Delaware.

More than 21 years elapsed between the beginning of construction on the first span and the completion of the twin.

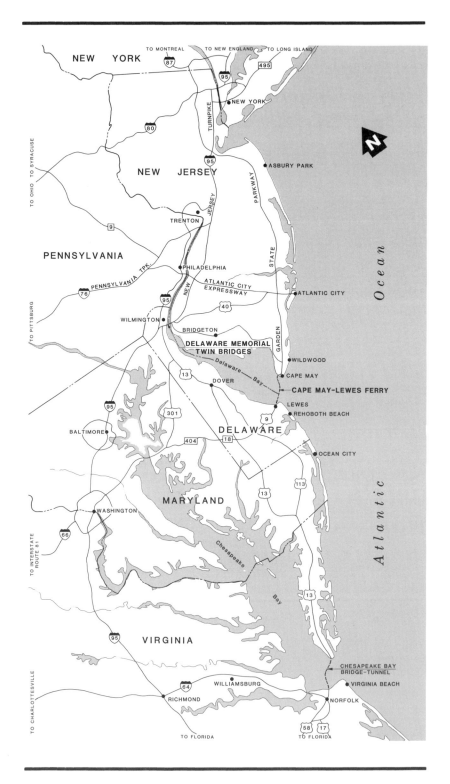

CHAPTER 1

CROSSING
THE DELAWARE

When George Washington crossed the Delaware River on December 25, 1776, the mere thought of a bridge over this most important waterway on the east coast of the United States was far from anyone's mind.

In fact, at that time in history, there were no bridges spanning the 296 miles of the Delaware River from its origins in New York State to its southern limits which meet the Atlantic Ocean.

Nor was there a need for bridges or crossings as we now know them. With a smaller population, land transportation was then limited to horses, wagons, and the like. When one had to cross a river, one forded it or crossed by ferry vessel.

Today, the Delaware River is laced by many bridges, from small, two-lane overpasses to railroad trestles to multi-lane, interstate highways. Bridges have replaced the privately operated ferry boats which once transported travelers. Now, the only ferry crossing the Delaware is at the southern most point, where the Cape May, New Jersey-Lewes, Delaware ferry vessels travel back and forth across the Delaware Bay seven days a week.

By the end of the 1930's several bridges crossed the Delaware River, but none connected the State of Delaware with the State of New Jersey.

In 1926, after many years and many different proposed structures, the Philadelphia-Camden Bridge was completed and opened to traffic. It was then the most southerly above-water crossing of the river.

And as we shall see, several different attempts were made to build a crossing of the river in the Wilmington area connecting to New Jersey.

In the early 1920's, a privately owned ferry was operated between New Castle, Delaware and Pennsville, New Jersey, as well as a ferry a few miles north between Wilmington, Delaware, and Penns Grove, New Jersey. Another ten miles further north, a ferry connected Chester, Pennsylvania with Bridgeport, New Jersey, which continued to operate until the Commodore Barry Bridge was completed in 1974.

Owners of the New Castle-Pennsville Ferry also operated a ferry service across the mouth of the Chesapeake Bay from the Delmarva Peninsula to Norfolk, Virginia (now the location of the Chesapeake Bay Bridge Tunnel, completed in 1964). The ferry owners, in an attempt to increase business, developed the concept of an "Ocean Highway" route for travelers from New York to Florida. The route was attractive for drivers who could use state highways in New Jersey, Delaware, Maryland and Virginia and on to Florida. Promoting the Ocean Highway also promoted ferry business, for the route required the use of both ferry crossings to complete the journey.

Where Does the Bay Start/Stop?

In 1905, the New Jersey and Delaware legislatures created a six-man commission, three from each state, to settle a long standing dispute between the two states: the dividing line between the Delaware River and the Delaware Bay.

In the 1600's, a deed from King Charles gave Delaware everything in a 12-mile radius of the courthouse in New Castle; this then created the state boundary line at the low water mark on the New Jersey shore. The arrangement left New Jersey crabbers and oystermen at the mercy of Delaware while on the river and within the circle limits, but under federal guidelines while in the bay.

In 1906, the official line was ascertained and marked with monuments. Inscribed on the monument on the New Jersey side is: "Mouth of the Delaware River. A straight line drawn from the centre of this monument to the centre of a similar monument, erected at Liston Point, on the Delaware shore, is the dividing line between the Delaware River and Bay ..."

In 1983, the Delaware River and Bay Authority after consulting with officials in New Jersey and Delaware engaged a contractor to retrieve the monuments from the river. New platforms have been built on each side of the river based on surveys which accurately designated the exact line on which the monuments are located. The restored markers were placed on the new piers in the latter part of 1983.

New Castle — Pennsville Ferry served as the link between the two areas before the Delaware Memorial Bridge was built.

In addition, the New Castle ferry also connected segments of US Route 40 in New Jersey and Delaware, the primary highway linking Washington, D.C. and Baltimore with Jersey shore points such as Atlantic City, and with northern New Jersey and New York City.

The ferry business grew rapidly as motor vehicle production increased, roads were improved, more people learned to drive, and travel became more popular. However, the ferry system could not adequately handle the surge of vehicles, and traffic delays and congestion worsened.

The lack of adequate service for people traveling through south Jersey and Delaware did not go unnoticed, and many efforts to build a bridge or tunnel were investigated; some private, others offered by various governmental agencies.

Interest for a new crossing originated more in the Wilmington area and in Delaware than in New Jersey, it is fair to say, perhaps due to Wilmington's urban setting. Certainly the constraints on trade and industrial growth were obvious. Regardless of the pressing need for a new crossing capable of handling the increased traffic, several factors complicated the planning process. One, in fact, smacked of an old fashioned feud.

Troubled Waters

For more than 100 years, the State of Delaware and the State of New Jersey disagreed on the location of the boundary separating the two states.

New Jersey insisted that the middle of the ship channel in the Delaware River was the boundary of each state and that title and jurisdiction rested at this location.

Delaware, on the other hand, claimed William Penn's grant (under which the three lower counties of Pennsylvania became the State of Delaware) assigned the entire river within a twelve mile circle from New Castle to the State of Delaware.

The many discussions and tentative plans for a crossing in this area were clouded by conflicting claims over the river ownership.

In 1929, New Jersey initiated litigation against Delaware to determine the boundary. After five years, the issue was finally settled when the U.S. Supreme Court ruled that within the twelve mile circle of New Castle, the Delaware River and the subaqueous soil thereof up to the low water mark on the New Jersey side belonged to the State of Delaware.

It seemed as if Delaware had won the feud.

Studies, Reports, Media Interest

Despite the economic depression of the country in the early 1930's, rapid developments in the motor vehicle industry made it possible for more individuals to own cars. Transportation was becoming vitally important to business and to the economy of the region and the nation.

Throughout the country, newly created agencies called "State Highway Departments" were being bombarded with requests to provide hard surfaces on dirt roads, widen old roads which had been built for the horse drawn vehicles, and build new roads which would easily connect the farms with the markets.

Cities grew quickly and suburbs began to form. Streets were widened, parking became a problem and people began to drive to work — the motor boom was on the way. The idea of a new crossing for the Delaware became increasingly popular.

The Wilmington Chamber of Commerce began promoting the idea. A Philadelphia Tri-State Regional Planning Federation in a 1932 report recommended the construction of either a bridge or a tunnel. Newspaper articles and editorials began to appear in support of the idea. Delaware, and not New Jersey, initiated the preliminary steps towards proposing a crossing project. Southern New Jersey's agrarian economy compared with Wilmington's rapidly growing industrial parks may explain New Jersey's apparent lack of interest at that time.

In May, 1940, Wilmington's newspaper, *The Every Evening,* printed a series of articles entitled, "The Delaware-New Jersey Bridge Project." Reprinted and distributed in booklet form, the articles traced the history of the bridge interest starting in 1917. The various legislative efforts in Washington were reviewed, as were objections to the bridge, projected tolls and traffic, and costs. Despite strong, local support, the probability of getting legislation passed authorizing a new crossing seemed doubtful.

In 1926, The Wilmington Deepwater Tunnel Company, a private corporation, also tried to get into the act by suggesting a tunnel crossing instead of a bridge. The proposed tunnel would have been two lanes wide, one for each direction. Plans for this privately operated project were defeated in 1937 by the Delaware General Assembly. The legislators felt strongly that such a project should be public rather than private.

Again in 1936, legislation was introduced in Washington to create a Wilmington, Delaware Bridge Authority to direct the construction, maintenance and operation of a bridge across the Delaware River near Wilmington. There was little interest in this legislation at the time, however.

During the same period, the Governor of Delaware appointed a study commission to look at the feasibility of the project. The commission recommended that engineering and financial studies were needed before serious consideration could be given to the idea of building a new crossing.

In response to the commission's recommendations, the state legislature authorized and directed the Delaware State Highway Department to investigate the legal, engineering and financial problems of a crossing.

The previously mentioned 1934 Supreme Court decision concerning the state boundary dispute with New Jersey encouraged Delaware to lead the way towards a solution to the crossing problem.

The report from the Governor's commission recommended that a two-lane tunnel or a four-lane bridge be built. Each was estimated to cost just over $16 million at that time. Also, the creation of a bi-state body to handle the project was suggested.

That suggestion opened the newly-healed wounds of the Delaware-New Jersey boundary dispute. Since the project would cross the section of the river already granted to Delaware, should not the joint agency idea be forgotten?

Opposition

The financial feasibility of the project was questioned as some wondered if it was too much for Delaware to handle. Also, while financiers had advised that proposed revenue bonds to provide funds for the project be free of federal income taxes to assure their marketability, this question had not yet been resolved at that time for a bi-state agency.

The project seemed to falter.

Another try was made in November, 1941, and again in February, 1942, when legislation was introduced in Congress to create a Wilmington Tunnel Commission which would have had the same mandate as the Wilmington Bridge Authority, but only to administer operations of a tunnel under the river near Wilmington.

This, too, appeared impractical. World War II and the rapid escalation in war-related problems prevented any serious consideration of this subject until the war was ended, when interest in the crossing idea immediately resumed.

CHAPTER 2

BRIDGING THE GAP

F inally, in April, 1945, the Delaware State Highway Department was authorized to construct, maintain, and operate a crossing of the Delaware River and to issue revenue bonds to defray the cost of the project in the amount of $25 million.

The legislation, among other things, also:

☐ Provided for the bonds to be tax free and declared that the bonds would be payable exclusively from tolls and revenues. The faith and credit of the State of Delaware was not pledged.

☐ Prevented the construction of any other crossing within 10 miles north or 20 miles south of the proposed crossing.

☐ Directed that the ferry service operating in this area be acquired.

Although a decision had not yet been made whether to build a bridge or tunnel, the General Assembly decided to select a name for the crossing. It was suggested that the crossing be named for President Franklin D. Roosevelt, who had died in 1945 at about the time the legislation was approved. But the Republican Governor of Delaware, Walter W. Bacon, firmly objected to the idea.

A reasonable compromise was quickly agreed upon: It would honor the men and women from Delaware and New Jersey who gave their lives in World War II.

The next important requirement to be satisfied was the enactment of the required New Jersey permissive legislation which was adopted in March, 1946. This legislation, among other things, provided:

☐ That New Jersey recognized the prior passage of the Delaware legislation concerning the crossing.

☐ That the New Jersey Highway Commissioner could accept title to land in Salem County necessary for the crossing. The commissioner was granted condemnation power, as needed.

□ That New Jersey granted its consent to Delaware to construct, maintain and operate the project and to charge and collect tolls in accordance with the recently enacted Delaware legislation.
□ That the act was immediately in effect.

This, then, settled the question about who would build the crossing and the circumstances under which it could be built.

During the legislative deliberations, the two states finally agreed that the crossing would indeed be a bridge instead of a tunnel as a more economical and satisfactory choice. Accordingly, the need for a War Department permit and for a Congressional franchise had to be addressed.

Federal Approval

Since the Delaware River saw such heavy commercial and military waterway traffic, regulatory requirements insisted that were a bridge to be built, it would have to be high enough and structured in such a way that ships could safely navigate beneath.

In fact, federal law in 1946 provided that bridges over navigable waters require an Act of Congress and a permit for construction from the War Department.

Congressional approval was obtained in July, 1946. Military approval would be more difficult to obtain, particularly considering the Navy looked warily on another bridge impeding traffic to and from the Navy shipyard in Philadelphia.

Federal authorities had strenuously objected to the construction of any bridge downstream from Philadelphia, because it might conceivably interfere with operations of the shipyard. At one time, a prominent War Department officer said to the press, "a bridge would never be permitted over the Delaware below the Navy Yard."

The Congressional act stipulated that the location and design of the bridge be subject to approval by the Secretary of War, Secretary of the Navy and the Chief of Engineers of the War Department. That would take some political maneuvering.

Another interesting stipulation of the legislation provided that tolls could be collected for 30 years or until the bonds were paid off, at which time the bridge was to become toll-free, with operations and upkeep to be absorbed by the State of Delaware. This is an important point, for in years following, this provision would cause the state to seek to reduce toll charges to delay the time when the state would have to assume maintenance of the bridge.

The War Department was presented with an application for construction of a bridge over the Delaware River in August, 1946, to be located 2.5 miles below Wilmington from Pigeon Point, Delaware to Deepwater, New Jersey.

Surprise.

Philadelphia Opponent

While there was little formal opposition to the crossing, nevertheless a Patrick J. McGovern wrote to the Secretary of the Delaware State Highway Department on October 18, 1946 of this protest about the crossing. He states:

☐ It is not a progressive project?
☐ Location of bridge too near TNT manufacturers and oil refineries in Marcus Hook.
☐ Could be used as a guiding post for enemy aircraft.
☐ Bridge will not serve purpose on account of atmospheric conditions.
☐ It is dangerous to all navigation. For instance, Philadelphia Naval Base, Hog Island Landings, oil tankers and the Port of Philadelphia.

Finally he stated that in 1938 he had protested the construction of the Battery Bridge in New York. A post script on this letter said, "Since I wrote atmospheric conditions in 1938, only one more bridge blew down, and great waste with the expenditures to strenghten others."

Mr. McGovern's opposition did not seem to have much merit.

The formal permit, granting approval of the location, clearances, and other design features of the bridge, was signed in March, 1947. The granting of this permit was indeed a substantial victory for Delaware and its bridge advocates. Only five months had passed between the application and final approval of the permit.

What changed the minds of the War Department officials?

Many have speculated on the reasons for the abrupt about-face of the military agencies concerning the bridge approval, but one must surely consider the following factor as the deciding one.

When the State Highway Department created a Delaware Crossing Division after initial legislation for the bridge was approved, General Eugene Reybold was appointed to head the new division. Ironically, or rather, in a calculated way, Reybold was a perfect selection. He was a Delaware native who had just recently retired as Chief of Engineers of the U.S. Army. It is probable that this single decision provided the expertise, the momentum, the political know-how and the military muscle to get this job done.

Many times one hears that the easiest part of building a road is pouring the concrete, and the same held true for the Delaware Memorial Bridge. Constructing the bridge would seem relatively smooth compared with the 20 years of turmoil and confusion which preceded the final project plans. More than 14 years had elapsed since any serious consideration for a river crossing had been made. The project that was estimated to cost $10 to $12 million in 1932, jumped first to $16 million in the 1940 estimate, and then to $25 million in 1946. All of these estimates were based on a four-lane structure. But even these numbers were to be changed.

Consulting engineers prepared a more detailed report during the five months the War Department permit was under consideration, which indicated that now the cost for a four-lane bridge would be about $40 million.

State Acceptance

The revised cost estimates meant another trip to the Delaware Legislature for permission to increase the bond issue from $25 million to $40 million. The approval, reluctantly granted, came in April, 1947, three weeks after the permit approval from Washington was received.

Records indicate that getting the General Assembly's support for increasing the bond issue involved some political backscratching. State legislators at the time were angry with the Superintendent of the Delaware State Police because he had decided to close a State Police station to save money. Since the State Highway Department was in charge of the State Police division, the legislators insisted that the Superintendent be dismissed before consideration would be given to raising the bond issue. Needless to say, the Superintendent was dismissed, the station reopened, and authorization to add an additional $15 million to the bond issue was approved.

Two months later in June, 1947, the first contract was awarded for subsurface borings of the river bottom, which would provide much of the basic data for the final designs for the bridge substructures.

By September, 1947, it looked as if the legislative problems were resolved, the money was authorized and approved, and all preliminary facets of this awesome project were finally ready to culminate in the actual building of a bridge over the Delaware.

CHAPTER 3

FINANCE

F inancing the bridge project was one of the most crucial and far reaching decisions made. Legislators were faced with three economic alternatives:

☐ A tax increase to finance a general obligations bond. This was quickly disregarded since anticipated heavy out-of-state bridge traffic would have discouraged support among Delawareans.

☐ A toll project with state-backed bonds. State support would have generated low interest rates, but there was doubt that the Delaware General Assembly could be persuaded to support the idea.

☐ Issuance of revenue bonds, based on the income from the tolls collected to pay for all the costs related to the project.

The revenue bond method was eventually chosen. Revenues from the bridge would be pledged to pay for the facility operations, maintenance, interest and amortization costs. Interest income on revenue bonds is not taxed, enhancing their marketability.

After the General Assembly authorized the method of financing, consulting engineers prepared a cost estimate for the entire project. At the same time, traffic engineers prepared an estimate of traffic and revenues to give legislators an idea of the expected income under different toll schedules.

A Revenue Bond Issue — What's That?

The legislation under which the Authority was created by the State of Delaware and New Jersey and consented to by the Congress entrusts the agency with certain purposes, contains the conditions under which the Commission can act, authorizes the methods of financing and delineates the overall jurisdiction, boundary and function of the Authority.

Subject only to the veto action of either Governor, and to the provisions contained in the enabling legislation, the Authority is nearly autonomous. And yet a list of conditions to be satisfied in the sale of one revenue bond issue contains the following:

□ *Certificates concerning the appointments of the Commissioners.*

□ *Bridge and Ferry engineering reports and certificates.*

□ *Resolutions authorizing the bond issuance.*

□ *Certificates of the Governor and Secretary of State concerning the Authority minutes.*

□ *Opinion of counsel relating to the bond issuance.*

All in all some 47 resolution certificates, reports or other types of documentation were prepared and acted upon.

The 1948 final cost estimate predicted the construction of a four-lane suspension bridge at a total cost of $40 million. However, other developments were taking place which would require changes in construction and planning.

In 1949, New Jersey officials announced plans for a new toll turnpike from New York to the southern part of New Jersey. The proposed Delaware Memorial Bridge (then just under construction) was a logical southern terminus for the turnpike. The decision to connect the new bridge with the New Jersey Turnpike was fortuitous for both facilities. Nevertheless, the additional traffic generated by turnpike users would require the redesign of approach facilities at extra costs. Also, construction prices were rapidly accelerating as the impact of the Korean Police Action was felt.

The original estimate included funds for the acquisition of the New Castle-Pennsville Ferry, but other urgent construction needs absorbed this money.

The single $40 million bond issue was therefore supplemented by two additional issues of $3.9 million in 1951 (at a coupon rate of 3¾ percent) and $2.5 million in 1952 (at a coupon rate of 2⅛ percent).

More Alternatives

Forty million dollars in 1947 was an extraordinary amount of money to raise for any construction project. But the Delaware Legislature supported the bridge venture and had authorized an increase in the bond issue from $25 million to $40 million to finance the crossing.

However, just as earlier cost estimates had proved inadequate, the State Highway Department soon discovered that even with the increase, $40 million was not going to be enough to construct the bridge.

Bids opened in the fall of 1947 for construction of the tower piers and anchorage foundations were well over original estimates. In fact, combined with the boring contract and other bids, it appeared as if a completed six-lane bridge would cost between $60 and $65 million - 50 percent more than the estimated cost and nearly triple the original $25 million estimate for a four-lane span.

Projected revenues for the bridge, which were based on a 75 cent toll for passenger cars and higher rates for trucks, were expected to generate adequate income to pay for a $40 million bond issue. The projected revenues at that time would not have supported a six-lane $65 million project.

The six-lane idea was explored even though the engineers' estimate for a four-lane span was $40 million. The more than $60 million cost eliminated it from consideration.

The decision was then made to proceed with a four-lane structure, which would have a total cost of approximately $40 million. The first construction contract for the bridge was awarded in July, 1948.

In June, 1948, the $40 million issue of revenue bonds was sold. It is thought to have been the largest bond issue in the state at that time. The basis for the bond issue was:

Estimate of Project Cost .... June 1948

Construction Cost......................	$29,351,000
Engineering and Administration	2,201,000
Estimated Net Interest	4,200,000
Contingencies and Ferry Acquisition	4,248,000
Total Project Cost......................	$40,000,000

Financial conditions in 1948 for tax free revenue bonds reflected interest rates that are phenomenal by today's standards. The $40 million bond issue sold in 1948 for a 4 percent coupon rate. The 30 year bonds were exempt from federal and Delaware income taxes. The faith and credit of the state was not pledged for the payment of interest or principal. In other words, the state was not legally bound to make good on the bonds. The income from the tolls collected was the sole source for the debt service.

Revenues

Would the tolls collected on the new bridge pay for this project?

Proposed investors had to be convinced that the money they invested in these revenue bonds would produce a return on the investment and the eventual return of the capital.

Just as structural engineers produced a cost estimate for the project, traffic engineers were selected to report on the number and type of vehicles which could be expected to use this bridge with suitable highway connections.

In their analysis, the traffic engineers had several elements to consider. A crossing in a major traffic corridor can be expected to attract large traffic volumes. The engineers could assume, for example, that the ferry users would continue to use the bridge. At the time of their study, plans for the New Jersey Turnpike had not yet been announced. This would have made a substantial impact on traffic projections. The proposed location would certainly attract the beach-oriented traffic during the summer months. And, the location could serve as a connecting link in the New York to Washington traffic corridor.

Two additional factors were considered. New facilities always seem to attract new users. Engineers had to estimate the number of vehicles which may be diverted from other routes for various reasons: time savings, distance reduction, lower toll, convenience, curiosity, or other factors.

And, the toll charge could have an impact on the traffic volume.

In 1947, traffic engineers submitted a report which predicted a crossing opened in 1951 would be used by 4.1 million vehicles in the first year, and at a 65 cent average toll rate, produce a first year income of $2.7 million.

As the project was delayed and construction costs changed, the report was modified. The 1948 version estimated that 3.7 million vehicles would use the bridge at an average 80 cent toll rate and produce nearly $3 million.

These expected revenues gave every indication that the $40 million bridge could be built and paid for by toll revenues within the 30 year amortization period, which encouraged investors to buy the bonds.

The estimates were revised again in 1951 as the second and third bond issues of $3.9 million and $2.5 million were required. This last report estimated that 3.65 million vehicles would use the bridge at an average toll rate of 92 cents (75 cents for passenger cars and higher toll for trucks), and that the first year revenue would be $3.37 million. This time, the New Jersey Turnpike traffic was included in the analysis.

The report concluded that if the projected revenue and operating expenses proved accurate, all bonds could be retired by 1962, just 14 years after the bond issue.

Costs

The total project cost had several parts. The major structure usually requires the majority of the total cost. In this case, the estimated construction cost of $29.3 million was about 75 percent of the initial bond issue. The cost estimate was based on a complete breakdown of the entire project: the design, quantities of materials to be used and unit prices of those materials.

When the final decision was made, for example, to proceed with a four-lane bridge, the amount of concrete needed could be calculated. The expected traffic volumes and number of trucks affected the decision on the thickness of the pavement. The weight of the pavement, the number of vehicles carried, the expected wind loads, the weight of the steel for the truss supports, all together determined cable thickness requirements.

Each section of the total project: the towers, the anchorage piers, the decks, the reinforcing steel, the trusses and all other parts were isolated and estimated.

In turn, the contractors who were qualified to build the bridge would submit their prices for each segment and for the entire project.

Other prominent costs included land acquisition for approaches on each side of the river, relocation of utilities, purchasing the New Castle-Pennsville Ferry, legal and engineering fees, and interest charges on bonds. These additional costs amounted to about $10 million, or 25 percent of the estimated costs.

So now they knew how much the entire bridge project could be expected to cost, and how the $40 million bond issue would be used.

Once An Engineer...always an engineer — Though Bill Miller serves as Executive Director of the Delaware River and Bay Authority, he has never given up his engineering hat. Here, he stands atop the cable near one of the bridge towers reviewing engineering drawings.

CHAPTER 4
DESIGN

Money, as they say, isn't everything, and though funding for the bridge project was finally approved — through a $40 million bond issue — there were modifications and new decisions still to be made on the final design of the bridge structure.

How many tons of steel or cubic yards of concrete would be needed to construct this long-awaited bridge? How many thousands of rivets, gallons of paint, or feet of cable would it take to erect a structure that would be the tallest ever built in Delaware, and also the sixth largest suspension bridge in the world?

First, adjustments had to be made on redesigning the original six-lane bridge plan into a four-lane model. With this decision made, the main suspended span of the bridge was established at 3,650 feet with a center span of 2,150 feet. There would be another 7,115 feet of bridge between land points and the major span, with a four percent grade on the approaches. At that time, there were only five other bridges in the world that had a center span in excess of 2,150 feet.

Now that it was known how long the bridge would be, it was time to get down to the specific details of designing the foundation, piers, towers, suspension cables, and deck work, all done in the context of the calculated stress factors the mammoth structure would be expected to withstand.

Foundations

A bridge is only as good as its foundation — and the foundation must be designed to complement the underlying natural structure. Before actual construction could begin, engineers had to analyze data gathered from ground borings to determine the exact geological makeup of the soil below ground level.

It was already known that the land formation in the area where the bridge was to be constructed was part of the Great Atlantic Coastal Plain. Typical characteristics of this area include low-lying flat and marshy surface land, with a ground makeup usually consisting of clay, gravel and sand beds above bedrock.

Certain tests determine the pressure which can be applied to these different types of soils, in turn guiding the engineers to determine the type of anchorage and tower piers to build. When drillers completed the boring on the river bed at the proposed bridge site, they discovered that even after drilling down 220 feet, they still hadn't hit bedrock. At 220 feet, they were still bringing up red and gray clay.

This information was surprising, particularly since boring for the Benjamin Franklin Bridge, just 30 miles upriver, revealed bedrock a mere 58 feet below the surface.

Now equipped with the proper geological information, it was decided to construct an open caisson foundation for the tower piers on the Delaware side of the river and an open cofferdam on the New Jersey side.

Sixth Largest in 1951

When the Delaware Memorial Bridge was opened to traffic in August, 1951, it was the sixth largest suspension bridge in the world. The 2,150 foot distance between towers established that position. The tower height of 440 feet above the water level, compares to 746 feet for the Golden Gate Bridge in San Francisco, 604 feet for the George Washington Bridge in New York, and 380 feet for the Benjamin Franklin Bridge in Philadelphia. The Benjamin Franklin Bridge, earlier known as the Delaware River Bridge, was the nearest bridge then in existence. It was built in the early 1920's and opened to traffic in 1926. This bridge has a 1,750 foot center span and cost approximately $37.1 million to build.

Caisson vs. Cofferdam

A caisson can perhaps be compared to a large biscuit pan with the bottom of the biscuit holes removed. The metal frame is lowered into the water and the material under it is removed by dredging. As the material is withdrawn, the unit gradually settles deeper and deeper until it reaches the preferred depth. At that time, the cells are sealed in place with concrete and the unit forms the foundation for the later stages of the total construction.

A cofferdam can be compared to a rectangular box crisscrossed with steel beams for lateral support. The unit is placed by driving vertical sheet piling into the river base, then dredging out the unsuitable material within the cofferdam. When the bottom is cleared, a concrete tremie seal is poured under water creating a bottom seal. The water within the sheet piles is then pumped out and the remainder of construction rapidly goes ahead.

Early Stages — The cofferdam construction. Cranes maneuver the permanent sheet piling for placement on one side of the cofferdam, which will serve as an anchorage pier.

After the sheet piling is driven in around the cofferdam, water is pumped out and a concrete seal is poured on the river bottom.

Cofferdams are constructed by driving four steel walls into the river bottom, dredging out the material within the walls and pouring a layer of concrete on the bottom. Then, water is pumped out of the shell and a top is poured to make a base for the pier anchorage.

Caissons, on the other hand, are built on shore and towed to the site. Each looks like an open concrete box with large steel shelves spaced throughout the box. The area below the caisson is dredged out and the caisson is lowered to the proper depth, then the bottom and top layers are filled with concrete.

Caisson Construction — The caisson anchorage was used on the west side of the bridge. Different in structure from the cofferdam, a caisson is made of a series of cells dropped to the river bottom then sealed with concrete. Here, a clamshell crane dredges material from the caisson cells.

Superstructure

The most recognizable and memorable feature in a large bridge is usually the superstructure — the part of the bridge which towers above the roadway for all to see. When you remember notable bridges throughout the world, you probably remember them for their unusual or recognizable superstructures.

The Delaware Memorial Bridge is identified by its tall, prominent steel towers suspending the sweeping cables which carry the road deck. It can be compared to a giant clothesline being propped up by two large towers rising high above the water.

Highest Points in Delaware

The Delaware Memorial Bridge towers are 440 feet high. This number compares to the 432 foot above sea level elevation in Centerville located in the northwestern part of the state, one of the highest land points in the state.

Tower Rising — An aerial view of the Delaware bridge tower as it nears completion. The Delaware anchorage and approaches are visible behind the tower.

Ironworkers drive rivets into the tower structure.

The two towers of the bridge are made of hollow steel boxes constructed one on top of another in a cellular fashion to reach the 440 foot height. They are connected at the top by a strut, and each tower has a ladder and three-person elevator from bottom to top.

Draped over the saddles atop each tower are twin cables which carry the load of the trusses, the deck, and the vehicles moving across the bridge. The cables must also withstand wind stresses. Most people may not think wind could play an important role in determining the structure of the bridge, and yet, the original planners for the bridge subcontracted with Princeton University to conduct a study of the wind pressures and the effects it would have on the proposed bridge design. Engineers did not wish to repeat the mistakes of the designers of the Tacoma Narrows Bridge. In 1941, this bridge, in the State of Washington, started to sway in the wind until the deck twisted and eventually snapped.

The bridge cables were designed to withstand all types of structural stresses. Each cable consists of steel wire individually spun across the bridge from anchorage to anchorage and back again, at a precise angle of repose.

Standing along mid-river, the New Jersey tower looms above the calm water of the Delaware River.

Engineers designed the cables in the Delaware Memorial Bridge span to consist of 436 singular steel wires banded together to make a strand. The finished cable would consist of 19 strands (or 8,284 wires) tightly banded by machinery into a 19.2 inch diameter cable that is again wrapped in a steel wire resembling a spool of thread.

Suspender wires or ropes of varying lengths hang from the larger cable connecting to the trusses at specified intervals throughout the suspended span. The trusses are strong enough to carry the concrete pavement and all the weight imposed on it by vehicles using the bridge.

How Strong Is Strong?

The design of the bridge is strong enough to carry the weight present if all four lanes were full of vehicles from one side of the bridge to the other.

Miscellaneous Design Elements

On the bridge deck, low level guide rails were planned so that motorists would have the opportunity to look up and down the river while crossing the span. A steel median separated the opposing lanes of traffic from which light poles were erected.

Since the Delaware Memorial Bridge is located in a climatic area subject to heavy, wet snowfalls and excessive ice storms, efforts were made to reduce the impact of these potential conditions on the bridge. Safety walks on either side of the roadway have open mesh grating for fast water runoff.

Maintenance and administration buildings as well as the toll booths were located on the Delaware side of the river, and were included in the original bond issue.

With all design elements now firmly on paper, ground boring data analyzed, and foundation types agreed upon, the time had arrived to begin construction, 18 months after the bond issue for the project was approved.

Progress, to this point, appeared to develop painfully slowly. But many legislative, financial and engineering decisions had to be made before the project could begin. Preliminary work on a project of this nature is sometimes as difficult as the actual construction itself — perhaps even more so.

The next phase of the bridge was something everyone could enjoy watching on a daily basis: the actual progress of the work.

My Bridge

To a native of Delaware, the Delaware Memorial Bridge is "his" bridge. To the son of a toll taker, the bridge is "his daddy's" bridge. Many people from the area share this attitude, and each one does so with justifiable pride.

Frequently, residents on either side of the river will call the bridge headquarters to report that the emergency lights are not on at the top of the towers, or that the highway lights should be on because darkness has already occurred.

And woe be it, if the time or temperature on the two display signs is not accurate. On the other hand, a good excuse for being late for work is to report that, "the clock at the bridge said it was only 7:25 when I passed by."

Magic Numbers

In one hour, the Delaware Memorial Bridge now carries as many vehicles as it did in an entire day in 1951, the year the bridge was opened to traffic.

Over the years, of course, not only have traffic volumes increased markedly along with population growth and motor vehicle registration surges, but also the construction of the twin bridge, which doubled the number of lanes from four to eight, provided the additional capacity to handle the heavier traffic volumes.

CHAPTER 5

FROM THE GROUND UP

Y ears of dreaming, politicking, legislating, planning, designing and redesigning preceded the actual construction of the Delaware Memorial Bridge. Some wondered if they would ever see anything crossing the Delaware besides the ferries which had served motorists for decades.

In the fall of 1949, however, doubters became believers as they witnessed floating platforms anchored in the river. The foundations were starting to go in.

The components of the project were broken into major contracts. They included:

☐ East and West anchorages and tower piers
☐ Approach river and land piers, embankments and super-structure
☐ Towers
☐ Cables, suspenders and suspended steel erection
☐ Concrete deck
☐ Approach roadway, administration building and toll booths

The west (or Delaware side) anchorage foundation was a caisson 95 feet by 221 feet in dimension. The steel structure was made in a shipyard near Camden, New Jersey, and towed downriver to the site in November, 1949. The caisson was lowered into position 93 feet below the water before the concrete seal was poured.

The east (or New Jersey side) anchorage was a 99 feet by 225 feet cofferdam embedded in the river bottom to elevations approximately 80 feet below water level before the concrete seal was poured at its bottom.

Previously, riverbed soil was removed from caissons by "sand hogs," or men who worked in the empty caisson dredging out soil by hand. As the soil was removed by hand shovels, the caisson gradually dropped inch by inch into the subsoil. This dangerous and time consuming method is rarely used today.

The underwater concrete pour for the caisson was the largest continuous single pour ever recorded during a construction job up to that time. Some 27,000 cubic yards of concrete were poured continuously for over seven days and nights.

Tower pier construction was patterned after the same caisson construction used in the west anchorage. Each caisson foundation was 69 feet by 116 feet. The west pier was carried down to a minus 87 feet, and the east pier to a minus 116 feet.

Fatalities During Construction

During the construction of the first span, six workmen lost their lives. The construction of a large, varied project inherently contains many hazards to workmen who transfer plans and specifications into physical features. The six men lost their lives in the following manner:

- *An ironworker fell on the East anchorage into the cable anchor bars.*
- *A carpenter fell from a floating concrete plant into the water during heavy fog and a fast running tide.*
- *A bridgeman using a riveting gun was knocked off a girder to the ground by the recoil of the gun.*
- *A bridgeman/foreman was struck by a crane cable and knocked into the water.*
- *A laborer operating a concrete buggy lost control and went overboard.*
- *A painter fell from a scaffold from the West tower.*

On the second span, three fatalities occurred. The first of these was at the West tower pier location early in the construction timetable. A workman, wearing relatively heavy winter clothing, fell into the river and did not resurface.

Much later in the project sequence, two workmen who were engaged in the pouring of concrete for the West Anchorage were thrown into the river when the form work collapsed.

It is truly regrettable that any lives were lost, but there is some consolation in the fact that the number is half the six lives that were lost in the first span.

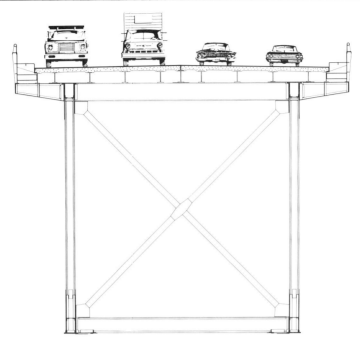

This engineer's diagram shows a cross section of the bridge superstructure, detailing the truss approach span. Though this is a diagram of the second bridge, the truss structure is identical in the first.

Another View — As the engineers' drawings are put into place, the above shows the orderly progression of steel beams on the deck truss under the bridge roadway.

Ascending Order — The concrete land piers on the New Jersey approach to the bridge fan out towards the river's edge. Atlantic City Electric Company is on the left.

Barges, cranes, sand and concrete float lazily beside the piers as their construction continues.

Once the foundation and anchorage construction was completed, the above-water construction began immediately.

It took 23,200 cubic yards of concrete for each of the anchorage blocks that support the two suspended cables. The anchorage blocks also serve as the connection points for the approaches to the main span in each direction.

All concrete mixing for the anchorages and river piers was delivered by barge. Cement and water were delivered to the mixer barges from shore locations.

Steel work for the approach spans was also delivered by barge, while steel used on the land was delivered by rail.

Once the foundations and anchorages were completed, erection of the above-water structure began at the bridge abutments and progressed towards the center of the river from each side simultaneously.

The tower steel erection, the most visible part of the bridge, progressed along with other sections of the project. Tower sections were fabricated and riveted on site. The towers were T-shaped and of cellular construction, connected at the top and below the deck by cross-wise struts.

Spinning the Cable

One of the most fascinating parts of the suspension bridge construction was the spinning of the cables. Just as building construction workers must work from scaffolding when erecting a new structure, the bridge workers had to have an intricate foundation on which to work. Before the men could proceed with erecting the cable, a scaffolding had to be constructed for them. A chainlink fence footbridge was suspended from the towers to the anchorages from which men and equipment would be supported. Timbers were linked underneath the fence to give it stability, and handrails were added. Once their worksite was completed, actual construction of the cable began.

Each wire of the 436 wires in each strand and the 19 strands of wire has a predetermined position in the cable. Each completed strand was adjusted for the correct sag for the proper position in the finished cable catenary curve. When the spinning was completed, the cables were compacted and wrapped with a red lead paste under the wrapping.

The suspender ropes were then hung from the predetermined cable band locations. While the final parts of the cable spinning work were being completed, the suspended span trusses and other steel work were being delivered to the site where the units had been assembled for erection.

The steel was erected simultaneously in the center and side spans from each tower location. The trusses were loosely connected initially so that the cable curvature and the final truss elevations could be adjusted to their final positions.

Cable Wrapping — Workers, standing hundreds of feet above the river on steel mesh walkways, prepare to wrap the cable.

◄ *Three bridge workers stand atop the New Jersey tower just before the cable spinning operation begins. Notice that handrails have not yet been erected on the workers' walkway.*

Suspended Animation — Quite an unusual view of the bridge construction, showing the two towers, the suspender supports and the truss work progressing simultaneously from each tower.

Bridge trusses are being erected. Balanced from the tower, the ➤ trusses are built outward each way— toward the center of the river, and toward each riverbank.

Finally, the deck is prepared. Reinforced steel is first installed in a grid formation before concrete is poured.

The original bridge administration building was completed in July, 1951. The building was expanded to its present size in 1965.

Looking toward Delaware, the completed crossing on the New Jersey side is located between the Atlantic City Electric Company plant and the Salem Canal. The Chambers Works of the DuPont Company is on the right.

Finishing Touches

The completion of the bridge was nearing reality. Any one of the thousands of office workers in Wilmington or Atlantic City Electric employees in Pennsville who had watched the daily progress soon realized that all the activity was beginning to look like a bridge.

By April, 1951, the steel trusses were connected. Only several more months remained before the bridge would be open for operation.

The last of the construction stages began — laying the four lanes of the roadway, each 24 feet wide. Work on the roadway moved from each side toward the center with different sections being poured in a hopscotch manner to maintain uniformity in weight distribution.

While the concrete was being poured on the deck, roadway approaches were in the process of completion along with the toll booth facilities and administration offices.

Because of a decision by New Jersey authorizing the New Jersey Turnpike — still under construction — to terminate at the Delaware Memorial Bridge, engineers had to redesign approaches on the New Jersey side to tie in with the new turnpike.

By the end of the summer of 1951, the bridge would be completed, save a few painting chores, and finally opened for traffic.

Vehicle Traffic Comparisons

In 1983, the highest usage of the crossing was surpassed. The new record number of crossings reached 19,633,074 vehicles in 1983, ten years after the 1973 gasoline crisis.

Vehicles per Year — Millions

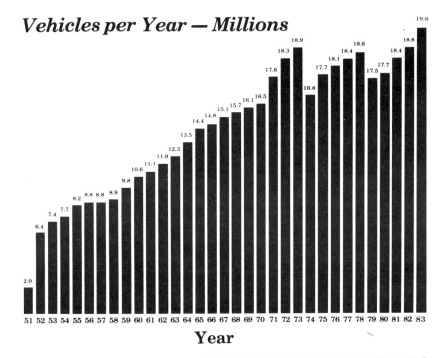

Year

Numbers

Quite probably during 1986, the 500,000,000th vehicle will cross over the Delaware Memorial Bridge. At the end of 1982, the total crossings reached nearly 430 million.

Oddly enough, during the years that the bridge has been open, the number coming from New Jersey into Delaware has always been unbalanced. About 1 percent more consistently enter Delaware.

Other important statistics indicate that the largest single day attracted 96,533 vehicles, the largest single weekend had 244,181.

Although the current toll rate for a passenger car is 60 cents, the average toll collected is nearly 90 cents, which indicates the impact that trucks and other commercial vehicles have on the revenue.

Grand Finale — The bridge is completed and opened for traffic August 16, 1951. Two million vehicles crossed the new bridge during its first few months of operation from August to December .

CHAPTER 6

OFF
AND RUNNING

*I*t was a day for governors to make speeches, for politicians to shake hands, for engineers to sigh in relief and for bystanders to applaud. The Delaware Memorial Bridge was opening for business August 16, 1951.

Governors Elbert N. Carvel of Delaware and Alfred E. Driscoll of New Jersey, officials from throughout the East Coast, and many spectators assembled for the dedication ceremonies on August 15th. A motorcade of dignitaries crossed over the bridge and back in a symbolic gesture documenting the official opening. Meanwhile, toll takers prepared for the hoped-for large volume of traffic beginning at midnight.

The bridge's first real paying customer was an inveterate fan of toll facilities who held the honor of being the first user of many bridges throughout the country. Omero C. Catan of Teaneck, New Jersey, the Mr. First of bridge and tunnel openings, paid the first toll on the Delaware Bridge at 12:01 a.m., August 16, 1951. It was a memorable day.

Since that first day of operation, statistics documenting the number of bridge users have been faithfully recorded and presented in various reports and statistical comparisons.

Traffic counts show that the bridge has been,and continues to be, a resounding success. Much more of a success, in fact, than the original planners had projected.

In 1947, traffic engineers prepared estimates on traffic volume and projected revenue for the new bridge. Using the most current information available, they estimated that 4.1 million vehicles would use the bridge during its first year of operation. A 1948

Opening Ceremonies — Invited dignitaries, community leaders from both Delaware and New Jersey and other guests gather to listen to dedication speeches August 15, 1951.

Maiden Voyage — Governor Elbert N. Carvel of Delaware is the first "official" traveler over the new Delaware Memorial Bridge, followed by Governor Alfred E. Driscoll of New Jersey.

Ribbon Cutting — New Jersey's Governor Alfred E. Driscoll (left) cuts the ribbon opening the new bridge as Delaware Governor Elbert N. Carvel looks on approvingly.

report reduced that earlier projection to 3.7 million. This estimate was made before New Jersey announced plans to build a new turnpike from New York to the new bridge. Traffic estimates were again increased in a 1951 report to 5 million after the turnpike plans were known. Based on a 75 cent passenger car toll, the bridge should have earned approximately $4.4 million during its first year.

Let's see if projections matched reality.

News Was Good

Though the 1951 projections were slightly overestimated, the rapid increase in traffic volume in subsequent years was hardly anticipated. Nearly 8 million vehicles crossed the bridge in 1955; the traffic engineers had projected a mere 4.4 million for that year.

Average daily crossings of 22,000 were being recorded in 1955, with the average creeping up to 30,000 during summer months. One holiday weekend, 43,000 vehicles passed through the toll booths.

The figures sounded exciting. But were they?

The traffic engineers' estimates were far short of the 8 million vehicles which crossed the bridge by 1955. In fact, that volume of traffic wasn't expected during the life of the bond issue (to be paid off in 1967) which financed the bridge.

More noticeable, when the 24 hour usage was documented in the first annual report presented in 1955, a little noticed sentence stated, "the bridge itself can easily handle up to 60,000 vehicles each 24 hours." Yet, in only four years, that number was rapidly being approached. What could be expected by 1960?

It was becoming apparent that too much of a good thing could lead to problems, for which a solution was not in sight. The bridge was beginning to approach its capacity limits and was barely six years old.

Success — Or Was It?

Along with the overabundance of vehicles using the bridge came tens of thousands of unanticipated dollars collected at the toll booths. The income generated by this high traffic volume was impressive.

When the bridge first opened, passenger cars paid a 75 cent toll; trucks were charged more depending on the number of axles. To assuage local commuters, reduced toll tickets were sold to daily users for 25 cents per ticket; 35 cents per ticket for less frequent travelers.

Using this rate schedule, revenue collected from tolls in 1955 hit $6.8 million — nearly twice what traffic engineers in 1948 had projected for that year.

Oddly, this news was not greeted with general enthusiasm by bridge officials. Here's why:

The federal legislation of 1946, which gave approval for the construction of the bridge, stipulated that tolls could be collected for 30 years or until the bonds sold to finance the project were paid off. After the bonds were paid back in full, the bridge would become toll free, with the maintenance and operations of the facility resting on the shoulders of Delaware taxpayers. Terms of the bond sale required that bonds be paid off as funds from tolls became available. This was a critical point.

This bonanza of revenue meant the bonds would be paid off in a matter of years, transferring bridge responsibilities to Delaware. Another point to consider was that the expanded traffic volume was bound to increase maintenance and operating problems for the bridge.

While Delaware officials fretted over what action to take on the pending problems, Maryland added more cause for concern by announcing plans to build an expressway from Baltimore to Delaware. At about the same time, Pennsylvania revealed it too had plans to build a new highway from northern Delaware to Philadelphia. Both projects would undoubtedly bring even more traffic to the bridge.

Acrophobia

The fear of height manifests itself pointedly for those travelers who cross large, high structures. This is a condition which is addressed frequently by the police officers at the Delaware Memorial Bridge whose lot it is to help these individuals.*

Genuine fear of height obviously excites and disturbs these people. They nervously explain their concerns to the officer; usually they do not wish to see outside their vehicle, either closing their eyes or dropping their heads down toward their legs.

The routine is quite simple: the police receive a telephone call or message, often from a toll collector requesting assistance for an acrophobia subject. Two officers are dispatched; one drives the victim in his/her vehicle across the bridge, the other returns the officer.

To satisfy this problem area is another responsibility which has been accepted by the Authority as a part of the services offered by the Delaware Memorial Bridge.

*For the past 5 years, the average is 3.5 acrophobiacs per week.

One Problem at a Time

In an attempt to solve the traffic flow problem and provide a method of financing, the Delaware State Highway Department and consulting engineers for the Delaware Memorial Bridge recommended in two separate reports the construction of access highways connecting the bridge with the proposed Maryland and Pennsylvania expressways. The report further suggested that these connecting highways be financed from revenues collected at the bridge, for it was the key point for interstate traffic passing through Delaware. At the same time, discussions for another bridge to handle the continuing increase in traffic were taking place.

Acting on recommendations of the consulting engineers and Highway Department officials, the Delaware General Assembly authorized the formation of a Delaware Interstate Highway Division to build highways financed with revenue bonds paid for by bridge tolls, and also to build additional toll crossings over the Delaware River.

Shortly thereafter, federal legislation was introduced which, if approved, would have cleared the way for an additional bridge to be built. It would also have permitted the continued collection of tolls on the bridge with the establishment of a fund to pay for operating costs of the existing bridge and construction costs of new access highways and a new crossing.

New Jersey, however, objected. During a hearing on the proposed legislation before the Congressional Rivers and Harbors Subcommittee in 1956, New Jersey representatives opposed the bill and asked that the two states be allowed to negotiate an agreement for the future.

Stalemate

New Jersey and Delaware officials drew the imaginary battle lines and negotiated for more than 18 months without reaching a mutually agreeable solution. New Jersey, it seemed, wanted the bridge to be toll free when the bonds were paid off, contrary to Delaware's proposal of continuing tolls to help finance a second bridge and access highways.

New Jersey countered that 30 percent of bridge users were residents of New Jersey and only 11 percent were Delaware residents. Therefore, they claimed New Jersey's interests in the bridge were three times greater than Delaware's, and revenues should be split accordingly if tolls were to be continued.

Delaware rebutted by pointing out that the entire bridge was built and financed by Delaware and that New Jersey had no interest in the project until it became successful.

New Jersey proposed that a bi-state commission be created to govern the interests of the bridge, and insisted that a majority of the members named to the commission be from New Jersey.

During these often less-than-friendly negotiations, an interesting proposal surfaced concerning the possibilities of a crossing connecting southern New Jersey with southern Delaware. New Jersey officials inquired about the feasibility of a ferry service across the mouth of the Delaware Bay connecting Cape May, New Jersey and Lewes, Delaware.

Using this proposal as a bargaining tactic, Delaware officials proposed that if toll collection could be continued on the existing bridge, Delaware would construct another bridge, finance a ferry operation further south, and divide funds with New Jersey to build approach highways for each new facility.

New Jersey agreed with this proposal, but continued to push for a bi-state agency to govern the river crossings. Negotiations came to a halt.

Bouquet or Ashes?

It is not unusual for the Authority staff to receive a request to permit someone to drop a bouquet of flowers from the center span of the bridge to an incoming passenger vessel or indeed to an incoming or departing naval vessel as they enter or leave the Philadelphia Navy Yard.

Somewhat unusual, however, are the requests in which the ashes from a deceased person through cremation are dropped into the river.

Both requests occur from time to time and are usually granted.

First Things First

Back to a more pressing problem: the bridge was simply making too much money. At the rate revenues were being generated by tolls, bonds sold to finance the bridge would be paid off soon. Delaware taxpayers had not expected to, nor were they willing to assume operating costs of the bridge.

Statistics compiled in 1956 showed that, after just five years of operation, more than $16 million of the $40 million bond issue had already been paid off from toll revenue. Planners had estimated the bonds would be retired in 1967, allowing Delaware ample time to plan for funding the operations and maintenance requirements of the bridge.

The most obvious solution was to reduce the toll charge, thereby slowing down the collected revenues and slowing down the rate at which bonds were being paid off. On June 1, 1958, bridge commissioners decreased tolls from 75 cents to 50 cents for passenger cars, and set a book of 50 commuter tickets at a 12.5 cent per ticket rate.

While the reduced tolls appeared to have a direct effect on reducing revenues for a time, the toll reduction in all probability increased traffic volume on the bridge. Before long, revenues were again climbing.

Less than two years later, bridge commissioners were forced to reduce tolls a second time. This reduction proved to be the lowest ever in the bridge's history. This second reduction set passenger tickets at a quarter and commuter tickets at a dime.

Traffic, however, was one thing commissioners could not reduce. The four-lane bridge built to handle normal daily traffic flow was being pushed towards its limits, particularly on summer weekends. Minor accidents, flat tires, and other mishaps on the bridge caused major tieups.

It was clear that additional facilities were desperately needed.

Bi-State Negotiations

In June, 1958, Delaware Governor J. Caleb Boggs and New Jersey Governor Robert Meyner agreed to name a committee of conferees for each state to negotiate an agreement. This proved to be the decision which led to the solution of the impasse.

While bridge officials struggled to solve the day to day operating problems, representatives from both Delaware and New Jersey began their negotiations on the future of the bridge and other potential crossings of the Delaware River.

Christmas Wreath

For several years between the late 1950's and the early 1960's, the bridge users and many people in Delaware received a special treat as the Christmas holidays approached.

The management of the single span thought that the strut connecting the top of the towers would be a suitable place for a large illuminated Christmas wreath to be seen by those who crossed the bridge and by those near it in Delaware.

The wreath, prepared by an outdoor advertising company, was made of steel sheets on which the wreath design was painted and the lighting arranged around the circumference.

As it illuminated the December sky, there were many favorable comments received concerning it. Unfortunately, the large unit, some 25 feet in diameter, had to be hoisted to and from the towers each year. There was always concern about an accident and, as the years passed, the interest in the project seemed to lessen. Finally the twin bridge construction, with the two sets of towers, provided a satisfactory reason to conclude a pleasant interlude at Christmas: the wreath on the Delaware Memorial Bridge.

The Compact

Between 1957 and 1959, a group of conferees representing New Jersey and Delaware met frequently to devise and recommend a plan to (a) jointly operate the Delaware Memorial Bridge, (b) to construct a second bridge and additional crossings as needed, including a ferry system for the lower bay area, and (c) to plan, develop and operate related transportation facilities and projects between New Jersey and Delaware.

The agency, still in operation, consists of five members from each state. In New Jersey, one is required for Salem County, Cumberland County, Cape May County and Atlantic County. The fifth is an at-large member.

In Delaware, two members come from New Castle County, two from Sussex County and one from Kent County.

In both states, not more than three of one political party may serve at any time. In each state, the terms are for five years, so that normally a member could be replaced or reappointed in each state each year. However, a member continues service until he is replaced by the Governor and confirmed by the respective State Senate.

A quorum consists of three members of each state and the affirmative vote of three members of each state is required for any action. Each Governor has veto power over any action.

The Commissioners elect their own Chairman and Vice Chairman, each holding office for a two-year term, then rotating to the alternate state.

Other powers and duties are covered in the compact legislation. One of the more unique provisions is that the police force authorized by the legislation enables the Authority police officers to have, regardless of their residence, all police powers usually exercised in each state when involved in Authority facilities or projects.

The Authority is not funded by either state. It operates exclusively with the revenue collected at the toll facilities.

The two states eventually agreed to establish a ten member bi-state commission to be known as the Delaware River and Bay Authority. This Authority was to have jurisdiction over the financing, construction, maintenance, and operations of all crossings on the Delaware River between Delaware and New Jersey.

At last, there was an acceptable solution of which the conferees from both states approved. The new proposal had to be adopted by the legislatures of both states and then ratified by Congress.

By July, 1961, Delaware and New Jersey had approved the pact and in September, 1962, Congress granted its consent. The Authority was formally organized on February 3, 1963, consisting of five commissioners from each state who were appointed by their respective governors and approved by the state senate. Each commissioner was to serve a five year term.

CHAPTER 7

ACTION

O nce the Delaware River and Bay Authority was established, it wasted no time tackling the pressing transportation problems between Delaware and New Jersey. Disagreements and political hostilities which had plagued negotiations between the two states in the past were put aside as the bi-state authority worked to solve the traffic headaches of the bridge and to explore the suggestions for a more southerly crossing of the Delaware River.

At its first meeting, after opening remarks from governors of both states, the Authority elected a chairman and vice chairman and settled down to business. During that first meeting, the new commissioners authorized a new feasibility study of a ferry crossing between Cape May and Lewes, and voted to apply for a federal permit for the construction of a parallel bridge adjacent to the Delaware Memorial Bridge.

This new spirit of cooperation between the two states was indeed a better atmosphere in which to operate. Commitment to cooperation was obvious from the very first. New Jersey commissioners, for example, nominated the first chairman to be from Delaware. Gone were the barbs of earlier years. Officials were no longer whispering, "Oh, he's from the OTHER side of the river..."

Immediate Decisions

Though the new Authority itself enjoyed a harmonious relationship, some wounds still needed to be healed. Prior to the creation of the Authority, New Jersey, with Delaware in agreement, had authorized the preparation of a report concerning another crossing.

This report was distributed during the Authority's second meeting in March, 1963. It contained the findings of consulting engineers studying the feasibility of a new crossing between Cumberland County, New Jersey and Kent County, Delaware in the vicinity of Sea Breeze, New Jersey and Smyrna, Delaware. The study had been requested by the New Jersey Department of Transportation, with costs split between New Jersey and the Delaware Interstate Highway Division.

The report concluded that a bridge in this area was not economically feasible at that time or in the foreseeable future. At 1963 prices, engineers estimated the project would cost $114 million for a four-lane and $64 million for a two-lane span.

Reluctant to deal with the possibility of a second southerly bridge, though local politicians from central Delaware and New Jersey (both areas which would have greatly benefited from such a decision) pushed for it, the Authority agreed to postpone further investigation of this proposed bridge. Instead, they chose to devote their time and efforts to the construction of a parallel span for the existing bridge and to the initiating of a ferry service between Cape May and Lewes.

Paying for the Projects

With the Authority's decision to pursue the construction of a parallel bridge and a ferry system, the question once again turned to how to raise funds to finance the two projects. A quick solution was revenue bonds financed with increased toll rates on the existing bridge.

Accordingly, at that same March, 1963 meeting, commissioners increased bridge toll rates to the previous charge of 50 cents per passenger car. Local commuter rates, however, remained at 10 cents to satisfy commuters who obviously would have balked at an increase.

Roadway Advertising — This sign, put up in the 1950's told travelers along Route 40 at the Maryland/Delaware State line what to expect in 12 miles.

Trailblazers — These official roadway signs lead the way to the Delaware Memorial Bridge from as far away as 60 miles. The first trailblazers (left) were used until the mid-1970's when they were replaced by the new design (right). Most signs are located on Interstate 95, Routes 13 and 40, and U.S. 301.

What Happens to the Money?

Contrary to the impression many people have, the States of Delaware and New Jersey do not share in the toll revenues collected at the Delaware Memorial Bridge or at the Cape May - Lewes Ferry.

All funds collected, plus those earned from investments are retained by the Authority exclusively. They are used for the following purposes:

☐ To pay the interest on the revenue bonds which paid for the projects undertaken by the Authority.

☐ To pay for the amortization costs for the bonds on a fixed schedule. All bonds are due to be paid off in 2004.

☐ To pay for operating and maintenance costs for the bridge and ferry.

☐ To pay for other projects which, in the judgment of the Authority, are required.

If the Authority has unspent funds, they are deposited in the Reserve Account and invested by the Trustee.

If the reserves drop below 120 percent of the operating costs, the Authority will raise toll rates or reduce costs to satisfy this condition.

Quickening the Pace

Everyone was anxious to see the next phase of the new bridge and ferry system move swiftly. Engineers were chosen for the bridge project — then, the Authority's first priority. Bonding representatives were chosen for each state, depository banks established, public relations firms and joint attorneys chosen.

To the pleasure of all involved, the time schedule for construction of the second bridge was much different from the first. By the end of 1963, details of the twin span were neatly falling into place. Instead of questioning IF the bridge would be built, as with the first one, everyone speculated on WHEN this one would be completed.

By January, 1964, two engineering firms had agreed on a schedule of construction for the new bridge. Approval for the second span had already been received from the Army Corps of Engineers, just months after the request had been submitted.

There was little if any opposition to the new bridge project. When the Corps of Engineers solicited public comment on the project, the only known reply came from a Delaware state senator who had served on the committee which helped create the Authority. The senator suggested consideration be given to putting the bridge further downstream. His suggestion, however, received minimal attention or support.

The first construction contract for towers, piers and anchorage blocks was advertised for bids that same January, though funding for the project had not yet been determined. Everyone concerned pushed for the project to proceed on schedule.

Bids for the first construction contract were opened in February, 1964, but the Authority decided to postpone awarding the contract until April when preliminary arrangements for the bond sale were to be reviewed.

Another Offer

Before bridge commissioners had time to award the first construction contract, an innovative proposal was placed before them in early 1964 requiring serious consideration.

Bethlehem Steel Company proposed to build the bridge, approaches, and a new office building for a lump sum price of $72.5 million if no other competitive bids were accepted from outside firms. Engineers estimated the entire project would cost approximately $70 million — close to Bethlehem's bid.

In a special meeting between the governors of New Jersey and Delaware, it was decided to decline Bethlehem's offer. The Authority proceeded with receiving competitive bids for each segment of the project.

Icicles

At one time only, in the middle of the 1960's there was a weather situation when a cold rain spell and a sudden temperature drop produced large icicles hanging from the cables on the first bridge.

These huge icicles could not and did not damage the structure. However, on the four lane span, the then prevailing wind was blowing the icicles from the cable and some of them were dropping into the right hand lane for New Jersey bound traffic. As soon as it was known, the police diverted traffic from this lane.

Before the traffic change, however, the sight of the huge icicles, some 10-15 feet in length and 8-10 inches in diameter at the widest point, created a spectacular sight for motorists. Many of them, unaware of the danger, slowed their vehicles to obtain a better view and looked upward through the front window — a most dangerous position at that time.

Fortunately, this one-time event produced no serious accidents. Even if it should occur again, the lane control system on the twin spans will enable preventative measures to be taken much more rapidly.

The Bethlehem proposal was based on a novel approach to the cable erection work for the suspension bridge. Instead of the traditional "cable spinning" method in which individual wires are strung along the entire span and later bonded together into the compacted cable, Bethlehem had proposed a method of pre-packaging the strands of steel wires in a warehouse. The strands, cut to precalculated lengths, would then be delivered to the site where the final bonding would take place. This new method had not been used before in any project as large as the proposed bridge, and was greeted with skepticism by bridge engineers. A more conservative approach of a proven method seemed more appropriate for a project of this size and importance.

Jumpers

Almost all major structures in the world and certainly those located near population centers become accessories for a seldom talked about group of people: jumpers.

From 1951 until the end of 1983, 77 people had jumped from the bridge into the Delaware River. In 1976, there were nine jumpers; in six of the 30 years, no one jumped.

Of the total, 51 were male and 26 female, almost a 2 to 1 ratio. There have been no black female jumpers during this period. The age range varies from teenagers to one person in the 80-89 year age category.

There have been more incidents on Tuesdays than any other week day. April, June and July each had a total of ten jumpers. The most prevalent time is a tie between 1-2 p.m. and 7-8 p.m.

Perhaps most unusual is that there is only one recorded instance where a jumper survived the fall. In this case, the person was heard to yell for help after he fell into the water. A passing freighter heard the scream and relayed the information to a nearby tugboat. The person was not seriously injured in the jump.

In 1983, another person survived a fall. After an unoccupied car was left on the span early on a Sunday morning, the Bridge Police alerted rescue craft. The person was found shortly afterward clinging to a buoy in the river. The person said that he had fallen into the river after stopping to urinate. He also had left his wallet on the front seat of the vehicle.

The majestic towers of the Delaware Memorial Bridge seem to rise silently from the riverbed below.

CHAPTER 8

ONCE IS NOT ENOUGH

P rogress — rapid and efficient — was the key to the second bridge construction. The first construction contract for $14.1 million was awarded at the Authority's April, 1964 meeting. Resolutions were also approved authorizing the sale of $103 million which was to be used in the following manner:

Redemption of existing bonds	$12,250,000
Second bridge construction	70,000,000
Cape May-Lewes Ferry costs	12,650,000
Contingencies	8,100,000
	$103,000,000

Nearly 81 percent of the bonds sold in 1948 to finance the first bridge had been paid off from toll revenues in the first 12 years of the bridge's operation. This prompt schedule of repayment plus the revenue earning ability of the bridge made the bonds for this bridge even more attractive to investors than the first bridge. The financing plans of the first bridge had proved successful. Investors were willing for another go. The bonds for the second bridge had a 40-year term and were solely backed by income collected at the bridge and the new ferry. The 3.75 percent term bond rate in 1964 compared with the 4 percent rate in 1948.

So much concrete was used in the bridge construction that it had to be made on large platforms floating on the river and moved by conveyor belt to the construction area. These men are mixing sand, cement, stone and water for the concrete.

A Set of Twins

When engineers first designed the Delaware Memorial Bridge, the idea of a twin span was not part of the plan. Traffic projections made in the late 1940's grossly underestimated the volume of vehicles which would routinely use the bridge. Expansion of the bridge facilities had not been forecasted for many, many years.

Yet, when observers now see the two mighty spans rising in their splendor above the river, it is almost inconceivable that they weren't planned that way.

The first bridge was not designed with an option to expand for more traffic carrying capacity at a later time. There was no possibility of widening the structure, and adding another roadway under the original one would have violated the clearance requirements detailed in the federal permit. Even if this had been allowed, the tower design, cable, and existing suspender designs could not have supported that additional load. Another separate crossing was the only reasonable alternative.

There was considerable discussion as to where the second bridge should be built. The idea of a parallel span was not automatically decided upon. In fact, the thought of another crossing downstream seemed to have its merits.

Huge section of steel tower is raised into place for the second bridge in October, 1965.

One factor which stopped commissioners from deciding upon a more southern crossing was that officials from both states were apprehensive about the costs of constructing additional approach roads which would have been necessary for another bridge farther south. Another persuading argument for a parallel bridge was that in the late 1950's, Congress announced that federal funds would be available to pay 90 percent of the costs for a National System of Interstate and Defense Highways. The Memorial Bridge was included as a link in that system. Though the bridge itself would not be eligible for funding, approaches to the new crossing in each state would be. This would mean a substantial savings to both states.

New Jersey also agreed to interchange the Delaware Memorial Bridge approaches with the New Jersey Turnpike, Route 130, and a soon-to-be-built southern section of Interstate Route 295 on the New Jersey side of the river. All of these factors pointed toward a parallel bridge construction.

Fraternal, Not Identical

To the eye, the two spans of the Delaware Memorial Bridge look identical, but their resemblance is basically cosmetic. While the general concepts of the bridges are similar, they are different in structure — more like fraternal than identical twins.

After the Authority and engineers agreed that a twin span should be built, designers set about planning a compatible structure. The second bridge's towers were geometrically identical to the first span, but beyond this, their structural "identicalness" is minimal.

One problem engineers had in designing the second bridge was deciding how far to build it from the first span. The further apart they were, the less chance of damaging both structures if an accident were to cause one of the towers to fall. But, approach roads to the bridge on the New Jersey side had to be sandwiched in between a large chemical company plant on the north side and an electrical utility company on the south side. Engineers placed the second bridge 250 feet from the first, which was the farthest distance possible in light of approach road restrictions.

Engineers did not design the second bridge differently from the first purely for the sake of difference. Most changes were a result of improved construction technology. For instance, new techniques in construction permitted the use of high strength bolts instead of rivets in the new bridge. The sound of riveting guns piercing the air was not heard during the second bridge construction. Also, fewer steel plates were needed for the new bridge, since steel was available in much larger sizes than in the 1940's.

The first bridge had four lanes, each 12 feet wide with a 3-foot wide median strip separating traffic and supporting the highway lighting poles. Openings at several intervals in the median

Close-up view of the concrete placement on the front walls of the New Jersey anchorage.

This worker operates an electric winch to adjust the individual cable wires.

allowed police and emergency vehicles to change direction, but regular traffic had to drive to the other side to get off the bridge.

Engineers modified the deck design on the second bridge to include four lanes each 13 feet wide with no median. The median was eventually removed from the first bridge and the lanes widened to 12 feet, 9 inches — nearly the 13 foot widths of the second bridge.

Even the underwater substructures of the two bridges were different. The first bridge used a caisson for the Delaware anchorage foundation and a cofferdam for the New Jersey anchorage.

On the second bridge, steel "H" piles support tower piers on the Delaware side while a soil bearing cofferdam serves as the New Jersey side foundation. The 29,000 cubic yards of concrete continuously poured to seal the base of this cofferdam was the largest ever done in the United States at that time. If you recall, the first bridge set such a record in 1949.

Anticipated traffic volume influenced engineers to design an eight-inch thick concrete roadway compare to the seven-inch deck of the first bridge. This additional load required heavier suspender rope and larger suspension cables. While there were 8,284 wires in each cable on the first bridge, the second bridge required 9,196 wires per cable.

Other differences included a water washdown system throughout the second span's length and a catwalk traversing its structural system under the roadway from one side of the river to the other. These features were also added to the first span.

Despite structural differences, the two towering suspension bridges connecting Delaware and New Jersey are recognized as the "twin" spans of the Delaware Memorial Bridge.

Construction Underway

Construction work on the parallel structure was rapidly advancing. Progress of the project was heralded in the 1965 Annual Report of the Delaware River and Bay Authority. The Commissioners under whose direction the work was being performed were pleased to report the accelerating activities.

Even so, the 1967 opening date was in doubt. Contractor delays, for one reason or another, had occurred. And yet as the construction advanced, the traffic volumes using the existing bridge continued to increase. The tie-ups during the heavy summer time periods, were, at times, vexing and exasperating to motorists. But, they could always look across at the cranes, trucks, men and machines, only 250 feet away and say "in a little while, these long delays will be soon forgotten."

The cable spinning wheel is being reloaded in the anchorage. Completed cable strands have been splayed into position on individual anchor bars.

Nevertheless, other details needed resolution. Some of them were critical, others less important. For example, the engineers had suggested that the design elements for the new toll plazas be modified to permit the use of "automatic" coin machines. These machines would permit the motorists to deposit the toll in a "basket" device which, in turn, activated a traffic signal system. Toll collectors were, of course, not required for this transaction.

Coins on the Pavement

The so-called "Automatics" are indeed a boon to toll facilities and to motorists. These are the popular machines through which tolls, usually coins or tokens, are deposited in a container to allow the patron to pay the toll charge and not have to wait for change.

The machines have mechanisms which automatically count the coins deposited and then flash a signal authorizing the vehicle whose driver has paid the toll to proceed.

From time to time, however, the operator does not "hit the basket." In these cases the coins, instead of being processed by the automatic counting machines end up on the pavement adjacent to the toll collection equipment. In turn the signal authorizing the driver to proceed is not activated. The driver then either leaves his vehicle to retrieve the money (not recommended) or leaves the toll booth and activates a signal indicating that the toll has not been paid.

In any event the coins on the pavement totalling $5,000-$6,000 a year are ultimately retrieved by operating personnel of the Authority.

The minutes of the Authority meetings in the 1965 period indicate that this suggestion was greeted with reservations by some Commissioners who apparently were concerned that the jobs of some toll takers would be affected.

Ultimately, reason prevailed, and the automatic machines were installed. The same Commissioners who questioned the idea, later admitted that the installation of the new, more modern equipment had been the wiser course to take.

Gradually, the project took shape. The 1966 Annual Report stated that the second span was 70 percent completed. More specifically:

□ A new administration building was constructed.
□ The two towers for the new bridge had been erected.

*Workmen balance precariously on the mesh walkway high
above the river water as they proceed with wrapping the cable.
The cable wires are first bound tightly, coated, then wrapped.*

A coating is applied to the cable wires before it is wrapped.

□ The cable spinning had started.
□ The new toll plazas were open.

Finally with a note of pride, the report announced that the 150 millionth vehicle had crossed the first bridge since the 1951 opening date.

More Progress, More Delays

Each month, the Authority received a progress report on the construction activities of the many contracts which were a part of the entire second span project.

In January, 1966, the engineers reported that they expected the twin span to be opened for traffic during the latter part of 1967. At that point, approximately $24.4 million had been spent on the second bridge. There were 20 active contracts in progress. They included:

Anchorages	$14.3 million
Towers	$5.2 million
Cables	$4.5 million
West Approach Steel	$4.1 million
East Approach Steel	$2.8 million
Toll Booths	$ .2 million

During 1966, the costs for the construction activity for a single month reached $3.2 million. Despite the rapid expenditure of money, however, the completion date was again moved back to "early 1968."

At the end of 1966, some $47 million had been spent on the project.

Delays on projects of this magnitude are hardly unexpected. The time estimates which are prepared well in advance are really "educated guesses." They are based on experience from prior projects, anticipated weather conditions and hoped-for delivery schedules. Labor problems and on-the-job accidents, among many other things, can lead to delays.

In this instance, the delay in the completion of the second span merely extended the time that traffic using the existing bridge had to put up with sluggish traffic conditions, particularly on the summer and holiday weekends.

On the other hand, the financial outlook for the project was improving. The delayed construction meant delayed payment to the contractors. In turn, this money being held in escrow accounts earned interest for the Authority. This interest money, earned during the second span construction, helped to finance the rebuilding of the deck on the first bridge, a part of the project not included in the 1964 bond issue. The building cost amounted to more than $10 million.

Looking east on the second bridge, the suspender ropes which will hold the truss and deck have been dropped into position.

One More Year

By mid-1967, about $57 million had been spent, over 2/3 of the project had been paid for, and yet, the completion date was still not yet certain. Contractors estimated a mid-1968 opening. As pleased as everyone was to get the project underway back in 1964, an air of expectancy toward the completion and opening of the new bridge was evident.

During 1967, it was announced that more than 15 million vehicles had crossed the existing bridge, the highest volumes recorded to date. Also a new single day record of 78,640 crossings was set on July 1, 1967. There was indeed an urgent need for additional capacity.

Preparations for the opening day began taking shape. In 1967, a contract for a traffic control system for the twin span system was announced. The system consisted of overhead gantries on which lane control signals and variable speed limit signs were mounted. Also variable message signs were erected on each bridge approach to advise motorists of traffic conditions on the crossing. For example, the sign might flash "Accident Ahead" or "Slippery Roadway" and the motorist could expect to see reduced speed signs or lane closures.

The Authority police operate the system from their headquarters. In addition to receiving information by radio from police and other Authority personnel, there are television cameras mounted under each tower strut enabling them, by remote control operations, to monitor traffic and even river conditions, continuously. The cameras can be rotated in any direction and can focus on a vehicle with enough clarity to read the license plate numbers.

Closely interrelated to the signal system are provisions for switching traffic from one bridge to the other if one span needed to be closed. For this purpose special "X" ramps are located on each side of the river. The complete detour arrangement can occur through a computer hook-up which will close one bridge and permit traffic on the remaining one to use two lanes in each direction.

As 1968 was underway, the date for the opening for the second span was set: September 12, 1968 was to be the ribbon cutting day.

There were still many things to be done. The paving was advancing rapidly, elevators were installed in the towers, navigation lights were added to the truss work, the cables were wrapped and the footwalks removed. Then the signal gantries were installed and the roadway lights erected. Painting was underway but would continue after the opening.

Finishing Up

The dedication ceremony arrangements were proceeding. The contracts for the renovation work on the first bridge were awarded to be started after the new bridge was opened.

The painting for the second span was being completed as were the contracts for the signal system, lighting and the final paving work. Work on the fender system surrounding the base of the tower piers was underway. All in all the major projects were to be completed before the end of 1968.

The total work effort for the twin span construction was not limited to the construction of a second span, although, of course, this feature is the most noticeable and is the most expensive part of the entire project. Other equally important segments of the completed facility are listed below:

☐ The New Castle Avenue interchange connecting with the bridge approaches had to be completely rebuilt.

☐ The Route 130 interchange with the bridge approach was also completely rebuilt, and with it, interchange connections between the bridge approach, the New Jersey Turnpike and Interstate 95 in New Jersey were accomplished.

☐ New toll booth facilities for each direction of traffic were constructed. For the first time in Delaware, automatic coin collector equipment was provided. Also tunnels were built under each set of toll booths and new toll collection administration facilities for each area were constructed.

☐ A new office building for the administration personnel was erected to provide space for personnel, engineering, purchasing, data processing and a new travel and information center, a new police office and a cafeteria for employees.

☐ During construction, the 40 acre site of land adjacent to the War Memorial, acquired in the mid 1950's, was the source of millions of cubic yards of material used in the embankments required for the second span. Millions of dollars were saved by the availability of this material. After the material was used, the property was again landscaped to its present contours and topsoiled and seeded.

The Night the Tanker Hit the Bridge

On July 9, 1969, at 10:26 p.m., the tanker "Regent Liverpool" chartered by Texaco, Inc. proceeding northbound left the mid stream channel and struck the fender system protecting the Delaware tower piers. Considerable damage to the fender piers resulted and there was some damage to the concrete pad separating the two tower piers. the preliminary damage estimate was $1,000,000.

On July 11, 1969, the Authority, through its insurance carrier, arrested the vessel at port in New Jersey until its owner, Texaco, posted bond in the amount of $3,000,000.

The contractor for the Authority, in the final stages of completion of the fender system, was immediately engaged to repair the damage caused by the vessel.

At that time, the deductible for the insurance covering the bridge accident was $250,000. Subsequently, the Authority received all costs of the repair.

The captain and pilot of the vessel alleged that a steering failure had occurred to cause the ship to leave the channel.

This event is the single major vessel accident at the bridge since the opening of the first bridge in 1951.

83

War Memorial

When the first span was dedicated in 1951, the Governor of Delaware in his dedication address stated: "How much more fitting it is that this Bridge be a memorial to the valiant men and women who have made the supreme sacrifice..." And the Governor of New Jersey responsed: "Compared to their sacrifice,...this Bridge, the sixth largest suspension span in the world is a puny thing. Nevertheless, the concept of the Bridge...represents a great achievement."

Since that time, the War Memorial area has been constructed. It contains the names of the veterans from New Jersey and Delaware who were killed in the service of their country during World War II and the Korean War. And currently, arrangements are under way to similarly honor the Vietnam War veterans.

Annually on Memorial Day and also on Armistice Day, appropriate ceremonies are held at the War Memorial site to honor these individuals.

Indeed, if for no other reason, the relatives of the 14,742 of service men and women whose names are enshrined at this location will always point with pride to the Delaware Memorial Bridge.

☐ Out of sight of most motorists crossing the bridge, field offices were constructed for the engineers and contractors for the second span. They are located under the approaches and remain as storage areas for bridge maintenance purposes.

☐ The one-way operation for each span necessitated the traffic control system for lane control purposes. However, as the first bridge modification work was under way, all traffic was routed over the recently completed second span. Since there was no median to separate traffic, the traffic was separated only by a double yellow stripe and was assisted by the lane control signals.

An outstanding feature of the entire project is related to the final project cost for the twin span. The estimate on which the bond issue was sold indicated that the second span cost would be $70,000,000. The final cost was $69,670,430.

Not so fortunate was the cost estimate for the first span reconstruction, which was expected to be about $5.0 million. The contract prices for this work totaled $11.5 million. However, interest earned on some construction funds and the tolls collected during the second bridge construction provided funds for this project without an additional bond issue.

The Twin Span is Opened to Traffic

The 1968 Annual Report starts out with the following:

> *"On September 12, 1968, the Vice President of the United States, Hubert H. Humphrey, officially dedicated the second span of the Delaware Memorial Bridge as the world's largest twin suspension bridge.*
>
> *"It was a day of excitement and crowds, of smiles and congratulations, of satisfaction for the completion of a big job well done. It was the climax of an engineering feat of major importance which began on May 28, 1964 when the first dredge moved into position at mid-river."*

The dedication ceremonies were highlighted by a motorcade led by Vice President Humphrey accompanied by the Governor of Delaware, Charles L. Terry, Jr. and the Governor of New Jersey, Richard J. Hughes, the Authority Commissioners and other officials from the two states.

And as a sequel to the 1951 dedication, "Mr. First" followed immediately behind in the parade. The two bridges, carrying traffic in both directions remained open for three days. Then the first span was closed for modifications. The euphoria of the new bridge didn't last very long. Repair work on the first bridge was to require another year of work during which time all the traffic was routed to the recently completed second span.

Medallion

As the completion of the twin span drew near in 1968, an idea was suggested which resulted in the minting of a special medallion commemorating the completion of the twin span. The medal was designed by artist Gilroy Roberts, who had designed the John F. Kennedy half dollar which had been a huge success.

The medallions were minted in silver, bronze and aluminum. A request to have a limited number of gold medallions was denied by the federal government at that time. The bronze pieces were given as souvenirs to special guests invited to the dedication service.

Silver coins were given to each Authority employee, numbered to agree with their service seniority with the Authority, and to other special guests and dignitaries. The aluminum coins were placed on sale for a nominal sum to the public.

Also, a local bank had ordered a supply of the silver medallions as a public service and placed them on sale at the time of the dedication. The response was tremendous — a line of would-be purchasers stood 3 and 4 abreast in a queue around a city block waiting to acquire the popular medallion.

The medallions are now obviously a collector's prize possession.

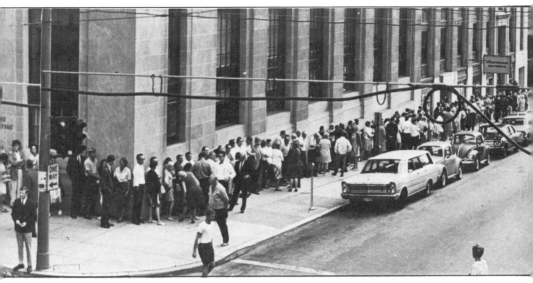

*Medallions, minted in silver, bronze and
aluminum, were made at The Franklin Mint
commemorating the opening of the twin span of
the Delaware Memorial Bridge.*

*Above: Hundreds of people wait in line at the Delaware Trust
Building on Market Street in Wilmington to purchase the
commemorative medallion of the Delaware Memorial Bridge.*

CHAPTER 9

THE FIRST BRIDGE RECONSTRUCTION

As the year 1968 ended, traffic volume continued to increase on the Delaware Memorial Bridge. A new weekend record was established when 204,000 vehicles crossed over the span on the August 14-16 weekend. Also 15,741,948 vehicles crossed during 1968, another record high.

The Authority, prior to the opening of the second span, had awarded contracts for the modifications of approaches to the first span to be accomplished between September, 1968 and June, 1969. After the contract awards, they then negotiated with the two contractors who were doing the approaches to also modify the center span.

This decision saved perhaps a year in the completion of the modification work. The contract cost for the modification was $11.5 million.

The first bridge, built in 1951, had been in service for some 18 years. The pavement, under the pounding of the many vehicles and the heavy trucks over the years, was showing the strain. The Authority, realizing that more time and money would be involved, nevertheless wisely decided to remove the existing deck in its entirety and replace it.

The three foot steel median strip which had separated the opposing traffic lanes and also supported the highway light poles was removed. At this time, each of the two separate roadways was crowned independently.

This meant that the drainage flowed towards the median strip and also toward the outside of the span. When the deck was rebuilt, the crown (or high point) was located in the middle of the roadway. On the first bridge, each lane was 12′ wide; on the second bridge, each was 13′ wide. When the 3′ median was removed and replaced with concrete, each of the four lanes on the first bridge was widened to 12′9″. (See Sketch)

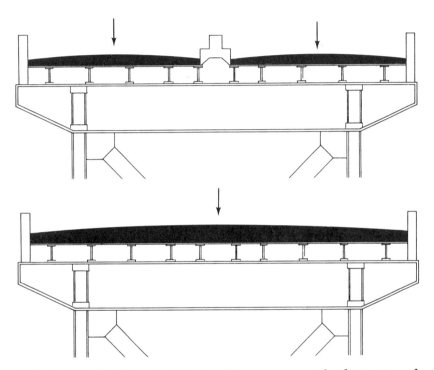

Original first bridge deck (top) — The crown was in the center of each lane for water to flow off both sides of each lane. When the bridge deck was reconstructed (bottom), the crown was made where the median once stood.

Of course, light poles had to be moved to the outside as they were on the parallel bridge; and other relatively minor changes were involved. Among these were provisions for a maintenance walk-way the entire length of the suspended steel work and approach truss system under the deck. This feature had been provided on the parallel span. On the first bridge, however, it was available only from anchorage to anchorage. Now maintenance men can walk across each bridge under the deck for inspection, cleaning and painting from river edge to river edge, state to state.

Another innovation built for each bridge was a water line span-ning the river through the suspended steel truss and girder sections. On a year-round basis, but more so in the summer, maintenance crews wash down the bridge sections. For many years this work was done with tank trucks parked on the roadway deck. The salt, sand and other chemicals frequently used for winter traffic assistance are harmful to the paint on the steel and to the concrete pavement. The decision to place 4" water lines across each span eased the job of washing away the chemicals. Each winter the lines are drained but need only a short time to be made operational during good weather.

Although not designed for this purpose, the water lines can also be used for fire fighting purposes, if required, on either bridge.

The lower chords of the trusses for the suspended spans are about 18" wide. They provide a narrow walkway for maintenance workers nearly 200 feet above the water. As a safety measure, handrails were attached to these steel members, so that workers can traverse them with relative safety.

Consistent with engineering efforts to make the Delaware Memorial Bridge one of the most modern in the world, a contract was initiated to provide a sophisticated traffic signal system which includes lane signals, emergency telephones on the span, sensing devices in the pavements to detect vehicle stoppages indicating accidents or other emergency needs, closed circuit television service from the bridge towers to the police office, and finally, variable message signs on each approach which inform motorists of traffic conditions to be expected on the structure as they approach it.

Changed Conditions

It was one thing to decide to reconstruct the first bridge in order to permit its use as a one-way crossing for the twin span. This decision had several long range implications to be considered as the project was to go ahead.

For one thing, the removal of the existing deck slab had to be accomplished in a manner which minimized the dropping of large concrete segments into the Delaware River and in turn perhaps jeopardize river traffic passing under the span or be a source of irritation for the steady dredging requirements currently under way to keep the river channel at the authorized 40' depth. Large nets were strung out under the truss to catch stray pieces of concrete. Primarily, however, the contractor cut the deck into segments with power equipment and hoisted the pieces on to waiting trucks to be hauled away.

Equally important to the engineers, however, was the retention of sufficient weight in the pavement area to avoid the establishment of stress conditions in some members under an unbalanced dead load. Consequently, the contractor had to use a checkerboard pattern as he removed sections of the deck. These removed sections were then replaced with new concrete to assure the continued loading required by the designers.

During reconstruction of the first bridge, the concrete deck was carefully removed. Nets suspended under the bridge caught stray pieces of concrete, stopping them from falling into the river and endangering river traffic.

The original deck had a depth of 7". The removal of the 3' steel median and the location of a single crown on the center line of the structure would provide for the free movement and full capacity of eastbound traffic on all four lanes of the new roadway.

The 1951 deck had been designed in accordance with 1944 bridge design standards for the trafffic types and volumes then anticipated. The new deck satisfied 1961 standards for much heavier vehicle usage. The new deck was 8" in thickness and the reinforcing steel weighed 50 percent more than the steel in the original slabs. The new deck would be able to carry a live load (vehicles) twice as heavy as the first bridge deck slabs.

The Welcome Banner

Most of the attention concerning happenings at the twin span is directed towards the motor vehicle user; after all, the bridges were built to enable those motorists to travel between the two states and points beyond.

But there are other points of interest. One of the most eye catching is the sight of large vessels moving up and down the river under the twin span.

The proximity of the Philadelphia Navy Yard facilities results in all sorts of naval vessels passing by on the way for maintenance work. They vary from submarines to aircraft carriers, battleships, cruisers and destroyers.

In the fall of 1980, the aircraft carrier, Saratoga, came up the river. At that time, the Authority joined other transportation facilities in an official welcome by erecting a 120' x 20' banner which proclaimed to those on the vessel: "Welcome! World's Longest Twin Span."

The same banner now has been seen during 1982 by the passengers and crew on the British liner, the QE2 on her maiden voyage to Philadelphia. Shortly after that event, the parade of tall ships was greeted by the emblazoned banner as they ended the long voyage from Venezuela.

It is now an expected procedure. The official welcome is the first expression to greet the vessels as they approach the metropolitan Delaware Valley area. In one way, the welcome provides an opportunity to show the maritime industry how much their contribution to the industrial and economic elements in our economy is appreciated.

The thicker concrete, the new structural steel members placed under the deck where the median had been, plus the new cat walks and overhead signal system, all added considerable weight to be carried by the suspender ropes and the cables.

The effects of the added load were analyzed and it was concluded that the changes would be acceptable in the most vital parts of the suspended span. The most impressive net change of slightly over 10 percent in the maximum deflection at the top of the tower (toward the channel) under dead load (structure) and live load conditions at the highest temperature would produce a 14″ deflection compared with a 12.7″ deflection on the original bridge.

Stay-In-Place Forms

Another feature which had been successfully used on the twin span was also used in the renovating of the first bridge. When the first bridge was constructed in the late 1940's, wood forms were used to support the concrete deck as it was poured.

Galvanized stay-in-place forms were used to replace the old wooden forms used in the first bridge deck. New concrete was poured in a checkerboard fashion to ensure proper balance for the suspender cables.

On the second bridge, however, the contractor elected to use "stay-in-place" forms. This meant simply that the corrugated metal sheets which supported the concrete were not removed after the concrete hardened. The galvanized steel will withstand rust for a considerable amount of time. Yet they can be removed, if desired, at any time.

As the story of the twin span construction activity is presented, it becomes evident that there are many details to be considered in projects of the magnitude of two world record size suspension bridges.

The ravages of time and wear required attention. This suspender rope from the first bridge, and many like it, obviously needed to be replaced.

Suspender Ropes

Hardly a household word today, the term "suspender" usually is associated with the devices used to support trousers. In this case, the suspender ropes have considerably more weight to be concerned about and to support.

A suspension bridge is inherently more flexible than other bridge types. The movement of the parts of the suspended structure are, in turn, susceptible to wear due to the constant movement.

The bridge deck is suspended from the two main cables by 276 suspender ropes, each 2 inches in diameter. As part of the modification work in the first structure, the contractor replaced 44 of the original ropes which were damaged by abrasion during the nearly 20 year service life.

The work was done with the utmost care under rigidly controlled conditions. Replacing the suspender ropes required that the dead load tension in the old suspender ropes be transferred to the new ones as exactly as possible. All of the other reconstruction work on the first bridge preceded the suspender rope replacement work to assure the designers that the total dead load was in place.

Another Dedication

Another pair of Governors from New Jersey and Delaware were on hand December 29, 1969 to attend a ribbon cutting event. Governor-elect William T. Cahill and Governor Russell W. Peterson participated this time. The ceremony marked the completion of the work required on the original Delaware Memorial Bridge to permit the initiation of one way traffic movement on each span.

The Twin Span, the largest suspension twin span in the world, carrying four lanes of traffic in each direction was complete.

There were six governors involved in the three dedication ceremonies since 1951 and an impressive list of legislators, commissioners and other officials in some manner related to the entire project.

Replacement Cost Insurance

The surge in construction costs has certainly skyrocketed. A quick comparison of relative costs can be seen when one compares the cost of the Delaware Memorial Bridge completed in 1951 at a total cost of $44 million, compared with the second span, a twin of the original, at a cost of $72 million completed in 1968.

Projects of this type, paid for by tolls collected from the users are usually the result of revenue bond sales which provide the funds for the construction. This was the case for the twin span construction work.

In this regard, the bond holder, the purchaser of the bonds, is protected by an agreement through which the bond holder's interests are protected. One of the features included in the agreement is a provision providing for casualty insurance in the event of a major catastrophe.

When the first bridge was opened to traffic in 1951, the "All Risks" insurance value was $25,810,000, which in turn represented 75 percent of the actual cash value.

By the end of 1982, the estimated replacement value for each span had risen to $193,000,000. The maximum probably loss which could be expected from any one catastrophe is now $70,000,000 which is the basis for insurance coverage limited by a one million dollar deductible.

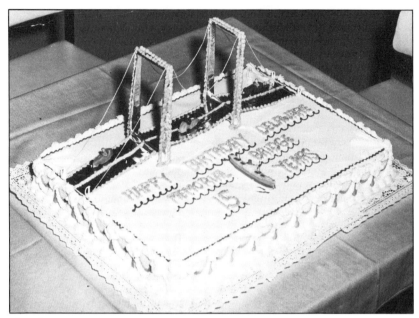

Anniversary Celebration — This cake marked the 15th birthday of the Delaware Memorial Bridge in 1966, just 2 years before the twin span opened.

One could say that the project spanned the years from the first bridge contract in 1948 to the opening of the twin span in December, 1969, nearly 22 years later.

The opening of the twin span coincided with the 1969 year end traffic reports on the bridge which again set new records. For the first time more than 16 million vehicles had crossed the river on the Delaware Memorial Bridge. Also, in that year, the 200 millionth vehicle crossed the span since the August, 1951 opening date.

CHAPTER 10

AS TIME PASSES BY

After the first full year of twin bridge operation, at the end of 1970, statistics continued to demonstrate that the decision to build a second parallel structure satisfied an urgent public need. Traffic records continued to be set. Now 16.5 million vehicles crossed the twin span and a single day record of nearly 80,000 vehicles was reported.

But of most importance to the user, the absence of traffic tie-ups on the span or the approaches because of accidents, flat tires, out-of-gas situations or similar causes were now completely eliminated. The police and maintenance crew working on the crossing could now heave a sigh of relief.

To illustrate the changed conditions, the bridge police reported that in 1970, despite more traffic than 1969, the number of traffic accidents was reduced by more than 50 percent.

1971-1973, The Numbers Soar

During 1971, 1972 and well into 1973, bridge traffic continued to increase, reaching an all time high of nearly of 19 million in 1973. The record number of crossings was destined to stand and not be surpassed during the decade of the 1970's.

A financial point of interest also took place in 1971. Under the terms of the Trust Agreement between the Authority and the

Trustee for the bondholders, the first series of serial bonds in the amount of $200,000 were due on January 1, 1971. Also during 1971, provisions were made to retire $300,000 of serial bonds on January, 1972.

In addition, the Trustee transfers funds each month to cover amortization requirements for the term bond retirements which was scheduled to amount to $150,000 in 1971.

With the amount of money deposited, at the then current price for the term bonds, the Trustee was able to purchase $215,000 in term bonds, thereby advancing the amortization schedule by $65,000.

Thus, the first steps were taken to pay off the $103,000,000 bond issue of 1964 which financed the construction of the twin span, the Cape May-Lewes Ferry and the payment of the remaining part of the bond issue then outstanding from the first bridge financing.

The total cost of construction for the modification work on the first span, nearly $12 million had been accomplished by the Authority without the need for a supplemental bond issue. The project was able to be financed from the revenue collected from the bridge users in toll charges.

One-Way Toll

Many of the bridges and tunnels in various parts of the country have one-way toll collection procedures. In the New York City area, there are several.

The idea is that those who cross the facility in one direction will ultimately return. Therefore, the tolls can be collected in one direction only and not on the return. This results in a lower operating cost to the agency and better traffic flow patterns for the user.

The idea has been explored at the Delaware Memorial Bridge but has not yet been implemented. Primarily this is because the proximity of the Commodore Barry Bridge would probably divert traffic in one direction from the Delaware Memorial Bridge and therefore the financial results would be unattractive.

If the four large structures in the Philadelphia area would join with the twin span Delaware Memorial Bridge in a one-way toll collection procedure, the result would, in all probability, favor the agencies and the public.

No one bridge could "go it alone", but as a group, the plan has considerable merit.

Comprehensive Inspection Plan

In 1972, the initial report on a five-year comprehensive survey of each structure was received. The first phase covered an underwater inspection of the 10 river piers of the first span and the 11 piers of the second span. It contained an analysis of the river bed configurations around each pier, settlement conditions for each one, and of the anchorage and tower piers, and a check of the verticality of the towers. The report indicated that the structures were in excellent condition.

Future reports will deal with other segments for each structure. At the end of the 5 year cycle it will be started again. Every effort will be made to continuously monitor the structural adequacy of the components of each bridge and the approaches.

Now Say Cheese — Quite an impressive backdrop for these fearless members of the bridge maintenance crew. Walking the cable, hundreds of feet above the river below, is a common days work for the crewmen who routinely must paint and maintain the bridge structures.   (Photo courtesy of News-Journal Co.)

1963 - 1973: A Decade for the Authority

The 1973 Annual Report of the Authority contained references to each year's activity since the creation of the bi-state group and its organizational meeting in February, 1963.

In a kaleidoscope of activity, the frenetic efforts to advance the twin bridge construction, the initiation of ferry service across the lower bay, and the myriad of details which had to be addressed and resolved, were outlined and hailed. There were changes in government, changes in Commissioners, changes in staff levels, but the projects continued to advance.

And then 1973 brought another unlooked for surprise: The gas crisis, the result of the embargo on oil products by the mid-east oil countries. When this occurred, there was an immediate reduction in travel as gasoline supplies diminished and as the price of gasoline escalated from 35 cents per gallon to more than a dollar per gallon.

Yet, new highs in traffic usage were set on the twin span for the first 11 months of 1973. Then the immediate impact of the gas crisis in December was felt. December, 1973 traffic was 15 percent less than the December, 1972 figures. Nevertheless, the present peak year figure of 18.9 million was reported in 1973.

1974 - 1978, After the Gas Crisis

When the traffic engineers prepared the estimates of traffic and revenue which could be expected to use the twin span upon its completion, they stated that several variables could affect their projection estimates. One of these took place in 1974, when the Commodore Barry Bridge between Chester, Pennsylvania and Bridgeport, New Jersey was completed and opened to traffic. The new crossing, about 15 miles north of the Delaware Memorial Bridge, connects many of the same arteries as the Delaware Memorial spans and in turn, can be expected to divert some traffic. The impact, however, was minor compared with the effects of the energy crisis resulting from the gasoline availability and price problem.

For the first time since the opening in 1951, bridge traffic had a reduction compared with the prior year. Total traffic was down 12.4 percent under 1973 and revenue was down 8.6 percent.

The difference in the percentage rates reflected conditions in the economy at the time. Commercial traffic was down only 4.5 percent which in turn reflects the more moderate revenue loss as compared to overall traffic reduction.

During 1975, the 300 millionth vehicle crossed the twin span, another milestone. The traffic volume started to improve over 1974, the year after the gas crisis started.

Since 1971, when the first amortization of bonds began, the Authority had retired $1,845,000 Term Bonds and $4,050,000 in Serial Bonds by the year 1975. This was nearly $600,000 ahead of schedule.

1976 marked the silver anniversary of the Delaware Memorial Bridge. In 1977, the early part of the year had record breaking cold weather and accompanying reduced travel. Yet, the year end figures showed that traffic volume had increased over 1976.

On September 12, 1978, the tenth anniversary of the completion of the second span occurred. Also during 1978, on July 1, a record breaking 96,533 vehicles crossed over the bridge surpassing the 1972 number of 92,209. Also although traffic again had a modest increase in 1977, the 1973 total was not yet reached.

The procedure for advance payment for Authority bonds continued into 1978, at which time the $103 million bond debt was reduced to $91,745,000, some $1,295,000 ahead of schedule.

CHAPTER 11

WHAT NEXT?

This brings us to the end of a narrative about a crossing of the Delaware. Crossings of the Delaware River date back centuries. The bridge crossings are most recent; the subject of this story, the Delaware Memorial Bridge, is unique because of its twin span configuration.

Opened to traffic in 1951, then the 6th largest suspension bridge in the world, now the twin span, finally completed in late 1969, represents the 14th largest suspension bridge crossing. At the same time it is the world's largest twin span.

There are many more things which could be written about this project. The anecdotes which are scattered throughout the book give some insight into frequent and at times infrequent happenings. Many of them lead to questions about other isolated topics.

When will the next bridge or tunnel be built? Probably not in this century. The studies which have been made by the Authority indicate that the Memorial Bridge and the Cape May - Lewes Ferry can handle pretty well the traffic which can be expected to cross the river in this time period. At the same time, there will indeed be other crossings, but not soon.

When will the Memorial Bridge reach capacity? Probably never. On one hand, the Bridge has more capacity than the approach roads leading to it in both Delaware and New Jersey.

Secondly, other crossings will certainly be needed if and when the bridge traffic reaches capacity condition — perhaps a doubling of the current average of 19 million vehicles annually.

A summary of the topics developed throughout this book covers a long time period and many people were involved in the many decisions which were made. Take a look at some of the major incidents:

☐ In 1926, the Ben Franklin Bridge was opened, the most southerly crossing.

☐ In 1934, the Supreme Court established the new boundary between New Jersey and Delaware.

☐ In 1941, reports said that a four-lane bridge or a two-lane tunnel below Wilmington could cost $16.4 million.

☐ World War II from 1942 - 1946 halted all bridge plans.

☐ Between 1945 - 1947, Federal and State legislators permitted a bridge project to be started.

☐ Between 1948 - 1951, the Delaware Memorial Bridge was built.

☐ After the 1951 bridge opening, the New Jersey Turnpike was completed and bridge traffic soared.

☐ In 1962, the bi-state Delaware River and Bay Authority was created to build a parallel span and a ferry crossing between Cape May and Lewes.

☐ The parallel bridge project was opened in 1969, the ferry in 1964.

The legislation under which the Authority was created is intentionally broad and permits the agency to initiate other projects in addition to crossings. In the public mind, the Authority is a political device created to satisfy New Jersey and Delaware interests to build a bridge and to operate a ferry. There are other points of view.

From the viewpoint of the Authority members who, appointed by each Governor, set the policy conditions for the Authority operations, a different picture emerges. They know that the bridge and ferry projects are public work projects which have been built to serve the public. They intend to provide this service well and it is quite evident that they have succeeded. They also realize that other things are needed.

Authority employees from both states are proud of their connection with the Authority. They readily accept their responsibilities and they handle them well. They represent a great contribution to the economy of both states.

There will always be another project to be undertaken at the bridge, a paving contract, a painting project, a new computer program or some other activity. Perhaps the one-way toll concept will be accepted to better serve the motorists.

Most importantly, the Delaware River and Bay Authority, the agency which has the responsibility to operate the crossing facilities between the two states, should reach out into other transport areas. Most noteworthy would be the development of terminal facilities along the river in each state. The Authority could and should lead the way in the development of a deepwater port in the lower Delaware Bay to service the entire Delaware Valley.

This subject can be another story at another time.

Appendix A - Persons and Patrons

Governors of the States of Delaware and New Jersey during the period of time covering the planning, construction and operation of the twin span Delaware Memorial Bridge.

DELAWARE

Walter W. Bacon	1941-1949
Elbert N. Carvel	1949-1953
J. Caleb Boggs	1953-1960
David P. Buckson	1960-1961
Elbert N. Carvel	1961-1965
Charles L. Terry, Jr.	1965-1969
Russell W. Peterson	1969-1973
Sherman W. Tribbitt	1973-1977
Pierre S. duPont, IV	1977-

NEW JERSEY

Walter E. Edge	1944-1947
Alfred E. Driscoll	1947-1954
Robert B. Meyner	1954-1962
Richard J. Hughes	1962-1970
William T. Cahill	1970-1974
Brendan T. Byrne	1974-1982
Thomas H. Kean	1982-

Appendix A - Persons and Patrons

Authority Commissioners

DELAWARE		NEW JERSEY
J. H. Tyler McConnell		Theodore C. Bright
William R. Murphy	ORIGINAL	Joseph L. Bowe
James T. Ferri	COMMIS- SIONERS	Bayard L. England
James G. Smith	IN 1963	Clarence B. McCormick
Howard S. Abbott		Thomas J. Gallagher
Alexis I. duP. Bayard		James L. Smith
Benjamin P. Shaw, II	INTERIM	Frank LoBiondo
Alfred F. Smith	COMMIS- SIONERS	LeRoy H. May, Jr.
Walton H. Simpson		John Vinci
Louis E. Edgell		Joseph J. Fabi
Dr. Garrett B. Lyons		Clarence B. McCormick
James Julian	CURRENT	William A. Gemmel
Ernest E. Killen	COMMIS- SIONERS	Angelo J. Falciani
Remsen C. Barnard, III	IN 1983	Walter F. W. Maack
Alfred Leo Donnelly		Jack Sparks

*The Commissioners of the Authority normally serve
a five year term. They can be replaced or reappointed.
Mr. Clarence B. McCormick of Bridgeton is the sole
charter member of the board still serving.*

Appendix A - Persons and Patrons

Delaware and New Jersey Joint Conferees

In 1958 the following individuals constituted the Bi-state Conferees Committee who recommended the creation of the Delaware River and Bay Authority as it exists today.

DELAWARE CONFEREES

Hon. J. Caleb Boggs, Governor
Garrett E. Lyons, Director, Interstate Highway
    Division, Chairman
Senator-elect Reynolds du Pont
State Representative Joseph B. Walls, Lewes
Clair J. Killoran, Wilmington Attorney
James L. Latchum, Attorney for Division and Secretary of
    Delaware Conferees

NEW JERSEY CONFEREES

Hon. Robert B. Meyner, Governor
Senator John A. Waddington, Salem Co., Chairman
Senator Charles W. Sandman, Cape May
Assemblyman John W. Davis, Salem
State Highway Commissioner Dwight R.G. Palmer
Vincent P. Biunno, Personal Counsel to Governor and
    Secretary of New Jersey Conferees

The Bridge Work Force

Many people are involved in the operation of the Delaware Memorial Bridge. They include:

11 — The General Manager and his staff of clerical, secretarial, accounting personnel and service department workers.

20 — The police force for traffic control, accident investigation and related activities.

45 — The toll taker squad which collects tolls, sells commuter tickets and gives information to motorists.

7 — The Travel Center and computer staff whose duties are in these fields.

53 — The maintenance crew. Work varies from bridge painting to snow plowing to grass cutting, along with many other jobs.

14 — Other personnel include wrecker operators, toll repairers, janitorial and cafeteria workers.

_____

150 — Total

The 1983 operating budget of $6.66 million includes $4.7 million in salary and employee benefits, $.6 million in insurance premium costs, and the remainder for material, services and utility costs.

The following people served as General Manager for the Delaware Memorial Bridge since the opening on August 16, 1951.

☐ John I. Cahalan
☐ G. Lester Daniels
☐ Charles T. Gallagher, Jr.
☐ Frank J. Horty
☐ Theodore C. Bright
☐ James C. Harkins

Appendix B - Bridge Specifications

Comparison of Principal Dimensions Delaware Memorial Bridge Twin Span

	FIRST STRUCTURE NEW JERSEY BOUND	SECOND STRUCTURE DELAWARE BOUND
Main Span, Suspension Bridge	2,150 feet	2,150 feet
Side Spans, Suspension Bridge	2@750 feet	2@750 feet
Total Length, Suspension Bridge	3,650 feet	3,650 feet
Delaware Approach Spans	3,899 feet	3,928 feet
New Jersey Approach Spans	3,216 feet	3,218 feet
Length of Structure, Abutment to Abutment	10,765 feet	10,796 feet
Delaware Land Approach	11,000 feet	8,870 feet
New Jersey Land Approach	2,700 feet	4,620 feet
Total Length of Project	24,465 feet	24,286 feet
Average Weight per foot— Main Spans	10,900 lbs.	14,000 lbs.
Side Spans	11,300 lbs.	14,500 lbs.
Maximum Pull in One Cable	17,868,000 lbs.	21,798,000 lbs.
Clearances under Main Span	175 feet vertically over a 1,500 foot width	165 feet vertically over a 2,000 foot width

The entire twin span project is nearly 5 miles in length. The crossing has been in continuous use since the opening day, August 16, 1951.

Appendix B — Bridge Specifications

Anchorage and Tower Data
Delaware Memorial Bridge Twin Span

	FIRST STRUCTURE	SECOND STRUCTURE
Delaware Anchorage		
Top, feet above water	162.0 feet	163.5 feet
Bottom, feet below water	95.5 feet	43.0 feet
Total Height	257.5 feet	206.5 feet
Weight Carried	194,900 tons	138,600 tons
Delaware Tower & Pier		
Top, feet above water	440.0 feet	441.0 feet
Bottom, feet below water	89.5 feet	53.0 feet
Total Height	529.5 feet	494.0 feet
Weight Carried	67,900 tons	42,800 tons
New Jersey Tower & Pier		
Top, feet above water	440.0 feet	441.0 feet
Bottom, feet below water	118.5 feet	53.0 feet
Total Height	558.5 feet	494.0 feet
Weight Carried	78,900 tons	42,800 tons
New Jersey Anchorage		
Top, feet above water	162.0 feet	163.5 feet
Bottom, feet below water	71.4 feet	68.0 feet
Total Height	233.4 feet	231.5 feet
Weight Carried	178,000 tons	181,300 tons
Lateral Movement		
Tops of Towers	0.65 feet	0.53 feet
Center of Main Span	8.90 feet	8.00 feet
Vertical Movement		
Center of Main Span	11.00 feet	10.58 feet
Longitudinal Movement		
Tops of Towers	2.36 feet	2.24 feet

The first bridge was designed by Howard, Needles, Tammen & Bergendoff of New York, New York.

The second bridge was designed jointly by Howard, Needles, Tammen & Bergendoff and E. Lionel Pavlo both of New York, New York.

Appendix B — Bridge Specifications

Suspension Bridges Around The World

BRIDGE & LOCATION	LENGTH	TOWERS (Above Water)	COMPLETION DATE
Humber Bridge England	4,626 ft.	510 ft.	1981
Verrazano-Narrows Bridge New York, NY	4,260 ft.	690 ft.	1964
Golden Gate Bridge San Francisco, CA	4,200 ft.	746 ft.	1937
Mackinac Bridge St. Ignace, MI	3,800 ft.	552 ft.	1957
Bosporus Bridge Turkey	3,522 ft.	541 ft.	1973
George Washington Bridge New York, NY	3,500 ft.	604 ft.	1931
Tagus River Bridge Portugal	3,323 ft.	625 ft.	1966
Forth Road Bridge Scotland	3,300 ft.	512 ft.	1964
Severn Bridge England-Wales	3,240 ft.	445 ft.	1966
Tacoma Narrows Bridge II Pugent Sound, WA	2,800 ft.	507 ft.	1950
Oakland Bay Bridge (2) San Francisco, CA	2,310 ft.	526 ft.	1936
Bronx-Whitestone Bridge New York, NY	2,300 ft.	377 ft.	1939
Delaware Memorial Bridge	2,150 ft.	440 ft.	1951
Wilmington, DE	2,150 ft.	441 ft.	1968
Walt Whitman Bridge Philadelphia, PA	2,000 ft.	378 ft.	1957
Ben Franklin Bridge Philadelphia, PA	1,750 ft.	380 ft.	1926
Chesapeake Bay Bridge Annapolis, MD	1,600 ft.	354 ft.	1952
	1,600 ft.	379 ft.	1973
Brooklyn Bridge New York, NY	1,595 ft.	275 ft.	1883

Appendix B - Bridge Specifications

Principal Quantities of Materials Involved in Construction Delaware Memorial Bridge Twin Span

Item	Unit	FIRST STRUCTURE Quantity	SECOND STRUCTURE Quantity
Earth Embankments	cubic yards	900,000	993,000
Cement	barrels	437,000	475,000
Concrete	cubic yards	291,500	293,500
Reinforcing Steel	tons	5,700	10,000
Structural Steel	tons	43,000	52,000
Suspender Rope	feet	56,000	56,000
Wire in Cables	tons	3,360	3,800
Wire in Cables	miles	12,600	14,200
Pavement -			
on subgrade	sq. yards	141,700	211,300
on structure	sq. yards	57,500	68,500
Total	sq. yards	199,200	279,800
Granite Protection			
for Piers	tons	4,600	4,900
Piles under Piers			
Timber	lin. feet	214,800	277,200
Concrete	lin. feet	16,500	39,000
Steel	lin. feet	—	277,500
Total	lin. feet	231,300	593,700

The primary reason for the additional material quantities for the second span is related to the higher design loads, thicker deck and slightly wider roadway.

Major Construction Contracts
Delaware Memorial Bridge Twin Span

	FIRST STRUCTURE Value $ Millions	SECOND STRUCTURE Value $ Millions
Foundations for Towers and Anchorages	11.6	14.4
Approach Piers and Anchorage Blocks	4.5	7.8
Approach Embankments	0.2	1.8
Erection of Steel — Approach Spans	5.4	7.8
Erection of Towers and Suspended Steel	6.4	11.8
Erection of Cables and Suspenders	2.3	4.8
Administration Building and Toll Plazas	0.4	2.6
Anchorage Tops and Deck Paving	2.2	5.3
Approach Paving	0.6	9.7
Land Acquisition, Engineering, and Minor Construction	10.6	13.1
Total Project Cost	43.9	79.1

The 1982 replacement value of each structure is estimated to be $193 million compared with the above totals.